PSL MODEL ENGINEERING GUIDE

MILLING for the MODEL ENGINEER

Patrick Stephens Limited, a member of the Haynes Publishing Group, has published authoritative, quality books for enthusiasts for more than twenty years. During that time the company has established a reputation as one of the world's leading publishers of books on aviation, maritime, military, model-making, motor cycling, motoring, motor racing, railway and railway modelling subjects. Readers or authors with suggestions for books they would like to see published are invited to write to:
The Editorial Director, Patrick Stephens Limited, Sparkford,
Nr Yeovil, Somerset, BA22 7JJ.

MODEL ENGINEERING GUIDE

MILLING for the MODEL ENGINEER

STAN BRAY

Patrick Stephens Limited

First published in 1990

British Library Cataloguing in Publication Data
Bray, Stan
Milling for the model engineer.
1. Workshop equipment: Milling machines
1. Title 11. Series
621.9'1

ISBN 1-85260-170-1

Patrick Stephens Limited is a member of the Haynes Publishing Group P.L.C., Sparkford, Nr Yeovil, Somerset, BA22 7JJ.

Typeset by Burns & Smith, Derby

Printed by The Bath Press, Bath, Avon

10 9 8 7 6 5 4 3 2 1

CONTENTS

INTRODUCTION

The lathe and drilling machine in one form or another have been known to man for centuries. True, these early machines were very primitive but they worked and enabled the human species to fashion wood and metal. The lathe utilizes a stationary tool and rotating workpiece, while the drilling machine has a revolving tool with a reciprocating movement and a stationary workpiece. The lathe can be made to rotate a cutting tool and by moving the workpiece secured to the cross slide we can use it for milling. Likewise a drilling machine could be used for milling if the work was brought against the tool and moved along it. That is so in theory at least but in practice, as it will be seen later, there is more to it than that.

It does not seem to be known when the first milling machine appeared in industry. Most work that required a flat surface used to be done on a planer, or a shaper which was much the same thing. This machine has an action rather like the carpenter's plane and can make a very good job of the sort of work for which it is used. There is one disadvantage, however. Because the tool is of necessity only made with a comparatively small cutting edge the machine has to be moved across the work very slowly and so it is time consuming. A shaping machine operator in a factory could frequently start his machine and then read a book for the rest of the day only needing to make minor adjustments to the depth of cut.

The milling machine was a far quicker proposition, but there were snags. Cutters were very expensive and also difficult to sharpen, with expensive equipment being required for that purpose. Most milling machines in the early days were of the horizontal type, the vertical mill not having really been perfected at that stage. The early horizontal machine was not that much more efficient than a shaper and so there was little incentive to change. The model engineers that were practising in those days rarely had either the cash or the space for the milling machines that were available, so improvisation was the name of the game.

The introduction of the vertical slide allowed milling to be carried out on the lathe and this became widely used. Milling heads which operated either from a line shaft or, very occasionally, from an electric motor were made in great numbers and the lathe cross slide was used as a milling table. These systems, whilst not quite so good as a milling machine, were quite efficient and many fine models were made using these methods. The milling head idea is still used today with the milling attachments which are available for most lathes. I propose during this book to discuss and explain these systems.

These days the milling machine or the milling attachment is commonplace in the home workshop. The vertical slide is still used by many enthusiasts who possibly do not have the room or the money, or perhaps the desire for a milling machine. To some, the ability to overcome problems is as good a reason as any for using the vertical slide. Mainly, though, this book will be dealing with the milling machine. Many modellers now obtain such a machine and use it, although it is doubtful if some ever really get the best from it. A milling machinist was a highly skilled man in the days before the engineering industry became computerized. It took a long apprenticeship to gain those skills and the model engineer cannot be expected to acquire them without some form of assistance. I hope that this book will offer that assistance.

There will be, as indeed there should be, a chapter dealing with safety. All machinery is potentially a hazard and learning to use the machine safely is as important as learning to operate it. This chapter will stress the use of guards around cutters to prevent the accidental catching of hands or clothing in rotating tools. However, the photographs in the book will show operations without the use of guards. The explanation for this is quite simple. With a guard in place it is very difficult to get a clear photograph of what is actually taking place. Also, some of the photographs will show 'mock-ups' of situations, since photographing real situations and operations as they happen is rarely possible. I must ask forgiveness from readers for these shortcomings but they are essential in order to produce clear illustrations.

The parts of a vertical milling machine

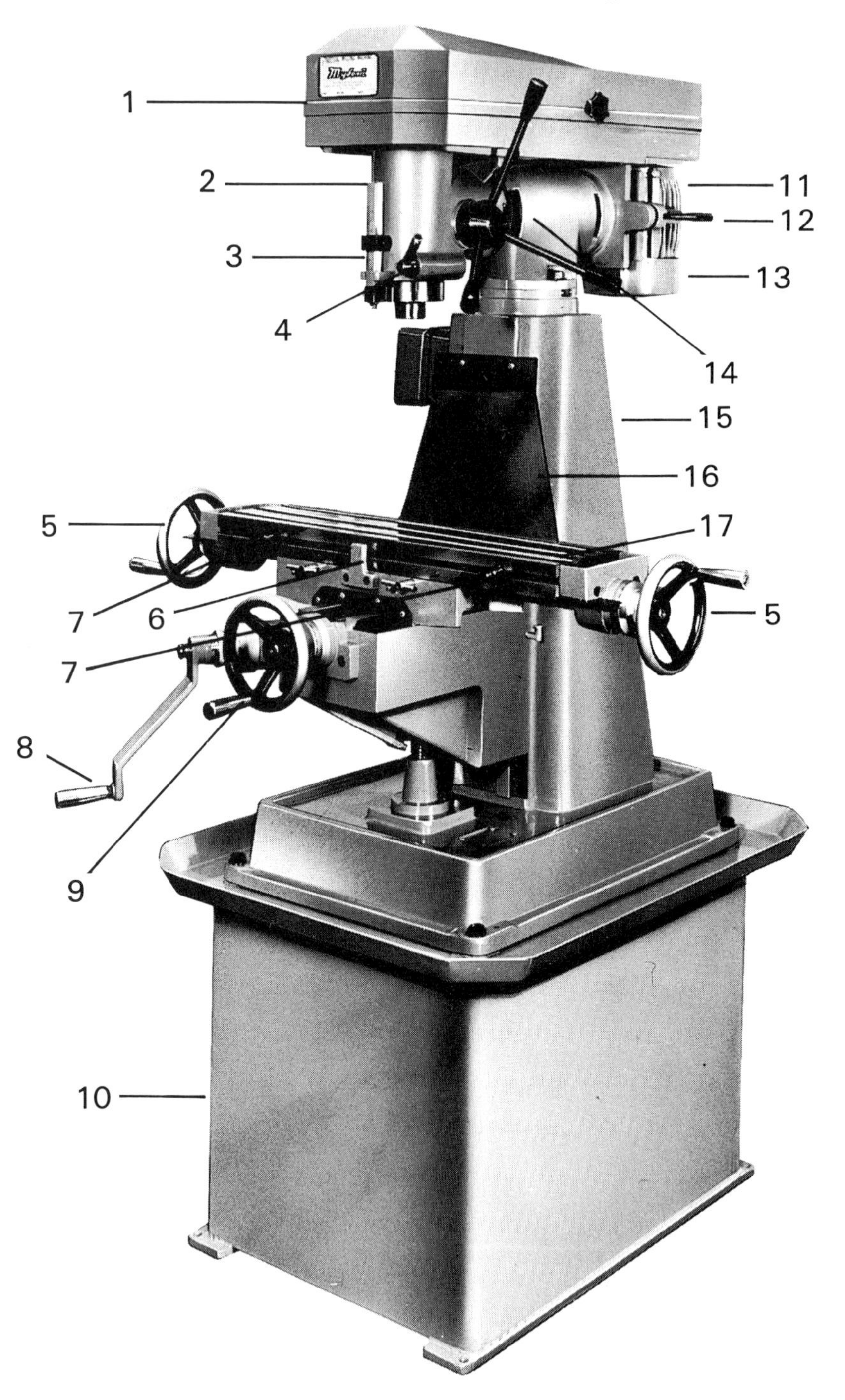

1 Top cover. This covers the belts and pulleys and is removable to enable spindle speeds to be changed.

2 Quill. This contains a mechanism which allows the spindle to be raised and lowered as required. The mandrel which runs in the quill is fitted with a means of securing milling cutter holders of one type or another.

3 Down feed stop. Not fitted to all machines, this is a useful device. It limits the downward movement of the quill to a set depth, allowing repetition of work where milling to a particular depth is required.

4 Quill lock. All machine movements not in immediate use should be locked in position to prevent vibration and chatter as well as a possible creeping movement of the component. This lever locks the quill in position after the depth of the cut has been set.

5 Handle for longitudinal movement of the table. A graduated dial is fitted to allow measurement of the length of cut. A loose collar is usually used so that it can be positioned at zero at the start of the cut. A locking screw can be tightened to prevent the dial moving from the required position.

6 Table stops for longitudinal travel. This simple device enables the table to be wound along to a predetermined point, thus saving the necessity for constant reference to the graduated dials.

7 Locking handles for the table's longitudinal travel. As already pointed out, when any form of travel is not required it should be locked to prevent the table creeping and avoid vibration.

8 Handle to raise and lower the table. Although the quill gives vertical movement, this is limited, so adjustment of the table allows the work to be brought to the point where as little downward movement of the quill as possible is needed. Excessive down travel of the quill can lead to lack of support and possible chatter. On some machines, instead of raising and lowering the table the whole of the top of the machine including quill, motor pulleys, etc, can be raised and lowered for the same purpose.

9 Cross travel handle. This moves the table across the machine. Again, this should be fitted with graduated dials.

10 Machine stand. This comes in a variety of types, some being fitted with cupboards to store tools, etc. Some of the smaller machines can be placed on a substantial bench instead of a stand.

11 Motor. This must have sufficient power for the operations which are to be carried out. It will usually be fitted with pulleys which, via belts, allow for spindle speeds to be varied.

12 Motor locking handle. If this is not tightened there will be considerable vibration when the machine is switched on.

13 Swivelling device. This allows the head of the machine to be swivelled at an angle to the vertical. Graduations marked on the head show the angle of tilt. Lower down is a similar device which allows the head to be placed at an angle to the column, which is an aid if angles are required to be milled on the work. Some machines have tables that swivel instead of the head, while many have no swivelling arrangements at all.

14 Drilling handle. This machine is designed to be used for drilling and milling. The down feed handle for milling is on the other side out of sight. A simple dog clutch arrangement allows each mode to be set as needed.

15 Column. The design varies considerably depending on the manufacturer. Many cheaper machines have round columns. The square type such as this has the advantage that the head alignment is always maintained. Also the table movement is via dovetails which makes for accuracy and rigidity.

16 Cover for the dovetail slides on the column. This is a rarely fitted device but can save wear on the vertical movement slides.

17 Tee slots in the table. These are a standard method used for the securing of work.

1 *TYPES OF MACHINE*

If, at least temporarily, we forget milling attachments for lathes and the vertical slide, and we consider pure milling machines, it is as well to think about what each type of machine will do for our own particular purposes.

The horizontal mill is just exactly what the name implies. It is a machine that has a rotating cutter laid horizontally and this cutter is moved across the work on a horizontal plane. This form of

A small horizontal milling machine. This type of machine can be purchased quite cheaply. It will be seen that the cutters are mounted on an arbor supported by an arm called the overarm. This arm must be able to move in and out from the machine. On larger machines the overarm will take the form of a heavy casting and will move on dovetailed slides with adjustable jib strips. A small machine such as this can frequently be purchased quite cheaply from machinery dealers.

A typical vertical milling machine which can also be used for drilling. The handle for drilling purposes can be seen at the top right-hand side of the head. For adjustments to the height of the milling cutter in relation to the work, however, the table is raised towards the cutter. The long handle on the extreme left copes with this operation. The machine is mounted on an industrial type of stand. This includes a tray to catch and possibly re-cycle cutting fluids. When a machine is bench-mounted without any form of tray, problems can be caused by cutting fluids running onto both the bench and the floor. This is not only undesirable but also dangerous as there is the possibility of a person slipping on the fluids.

A highly accurate Italian vertical milling machine by Gordini. It is designed for precision work and would therefore be very suitable for a model engineer. The head of the machine swivels, and unlike the previous photograph the head lowers and raises bringing the cutter to the work rather than the work to the cutter.

Right *A smaller type of vertical machine, the Emco FB-2, on a stand. Ideal for light work, the machine is very compact. For the purposes of the photograph the head, which is fully swivelling, has been set at an angle. The machine is not fully universal as it cannot be used with the types of cutters associated with horizontal milling.*

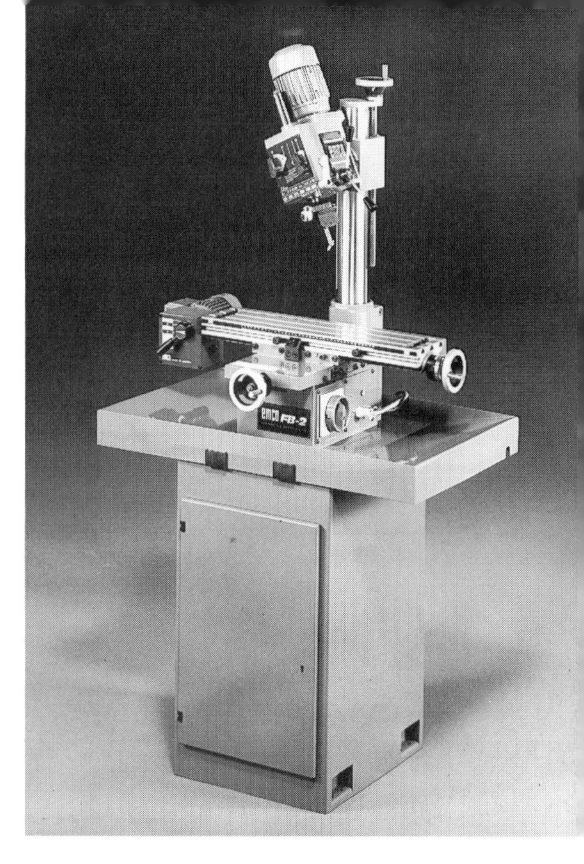

Below *Milling machines come in a variety of sizes and small ones can be very useful. This picture gives some idea of the size of the Cowell vertical machine which is very robust for its size and ideal for small modelling. The machine shown is a very early version.*

The modern Cowell machine has been updated to give ease of working. The operating controls for speed adjustment (by an electronic controller) are now on the base. This is an unusual feature as the vast majority of machines have speed adjustment via pulleys and belts, with the more expensive ones employing a gearing system.

The Sharp Mark 2 miling machine is one that was designed entirely with the model engineer in mind – it is a true universal. The pulleys at the back are for speed alteration when used as a horizontal machine. When used as a vertical machine, the cutters are held in a two morse taper collet system which is interchangeable with the Myford and many other lathes. This saves having extra tools in the workshop and a great deal of extra expense.

construction means that heavy cuts can be taken from the work if one so requires, and work is therefore carried out very much more quickly than with some other types of machine. With a little thought and ingenuity, the horizontal milling machine will carry out most operations that a model engineer requires. Sometimes, though, this means making special tools for certain types of work and this can be somewhat time consuming. This type of machine uses relatively large cutters which need special equipment for sharpening, and this too can be a disadvantage. Horizontal milling machines come in all sizes and there are some small ones available that can frequently be purchased second hand at very reasonable prices.

The vertical milling machine again works as the name implies. The cutter is held in a vertical position although the work basically travels still in a horizontal plane. By their very nature, vertical machines do not have the same rigidity as horizontal ones. However, they are often more convenient for many operations and suitable cutters can be purchased for carrying out a whole variety of operations which on a horizontal machine would require a special cutter to be made.The cutters for the vertical machine are also considerably cheaper to purchase than those for the horizontal variety.

The universal milling machine, strictly speaking, means a machine that can be used in either the horizontal or vertical mode.

The Sharp Mark 2 milling machine shown in horizontal mode; the machine is compact enough for a small workshop but still large enough for any work that most model engineers will want to do. More important still, it is very robust.

Almost invariably the heads carrying the cutters can be swivelled to an angle as well, and often the table can also be moved to an angular position. Cutters are the same as those used on normal horizontal and vertical machines. On the smaller universal machines, there may be some lack of rigidity. This does not apply on the more expensive ones which have a specially strong form of construction. Some machines are described as universal when in fact they are only vertical machines with a head that swivels. There are many versions of this type designed with the model engineer in mind, and whilst not suitable for very heavy work they are very versatile and therefore quite popular.

Vertical and universal machines come in a wide variety of sizes. Some of the very large ones weigh several tonnes, whilst some small vertical models designed specially for the model engineer can be picked up and carried about quite easily. There are always plenty available either new or second hand from which to choose.

2 BUYING A MILLING MACHINE

The two things most likely to affect the purchase of a milling machine are the price and the amount of space available for it in the workshop. These two considerations cannot be adequately resolved in a book since they concern each individual. I can, however, offer suggestions on other aspects to look out for.

Let us take new machines first, because what we look for in a new machine should also be considered when buying second

Worth considering for the small workshop or where the machine has to be put away after use is this small machine by Emco Ltd.

hand. Unless one is to specialize in a skill such as watch or jewellery making, it is as well to purchase a machine with as large a capacity as possible, whilst not sacrificing quality in any way. The table size is obviously important. Will it take the size of work we have in mind? Also does it have the travel we desire? It is possible to purchase a machine with quite a large table and yet find that the travel is so limited that full use cannot be made of it.

The height that the cutter can be raised may be of importance. Some milling machines are designed so that they may be used as drills; in this case a greater height of spindle will be needed than in the case of a machine designed purely for milling purposes. Whilst thinking of the table, it would be as well to try the machine out if possible, and in particular check for vibration at the extreme end of the travel. Sometimes this can be a disaster area, and whilst the machine is very rigid when the table is more or less central, the story changes completely as the table is taken to its full extremities.

This brings us to rigidity. It will be seen later that this is the most important thing in milling. There are machines about that leave something to be desired in this direction. Equally there are also machines that look comparatively small and yet no matter where the table is in use, everything is as rigid as it should be. The head too must also be rigid, and a machine with a small diameter column must be treated with suspicion because such a column is highly likely to be somewhat flexible which affects the head.

The question of the column is a perplexing one. A machine with a round column will nearly always offer advantages in price, but

A thing to look for when buying a machine are nice clear graduations on dials. This picture shows clear measurement taken a further stage with graduations along the table as well.

The type of older machine that can often be purchased very cheaply. This old Richmond is a universal machine, is fitted with a recirculating lubrication system and is very rigid. Although the table is larger than average, the machine is not as big as many with smaller tables. It is very heavy and this is one reason why it is unlikely to fetch a very high price. There is some damage to the table almost certainly caused through overtightening of a tee bolt or use of a the wrong sized bolt. This can be repaired by milling out where the casting is broken and screwing in a mild steel block. This can then be machined to conform to the table and the damage would be barely visible.

there can sometimes be pitfalls. If the head is raised on a round column machine can it be set accurately in line with its position lower down? This is certainly not always the case. However, that does not necessarily mean that the machine is of little use, it is just that when it is used that aspect will always have to be considered.

Most machines these days have motors of adequate power, but the spindle speeds they provide are worth thinking about. For good machining, the correct speed of cutter rotation is most important. Unfortunately this will depend on the various speed-changing facilities on the machine and so it will be unlikely to provide the exact speed. The more spindle speeds the machine provides, the nearer we will be to the correct one.

The arrangement for securing cutters may be important. On a horizontal miller there will almost certainly only be one system. Vertical millers, however, have a wide variety, depending on the construction of the spindle nose. Most have a taper of one sort or another, but do not forget that some form of collet must be used in this taper. It can be very advantageous to get a machine with the same fitting as your lathe mandrel. This will save expense and mean that everything is interchangeable.

The Bridgeport is a massive machine and fetches a high price even when quite old. If there is room for one in a home workshop and it can be obtained at a reasonable price, it is the pure Rolls Royce of milling machines, and is universal with a removable head. However, it would need a block and tackle to remove it.

So much for purchasing new machines, when one can look round and select at leisure. What of second-hand ones? Here the choice will have to depend to a large extent on what is available. The general condition of the machine is important. If the table has suffered from cutters being run into it, then beware—the rest of the machine has probably also been misused. Sometimes one will find a machine with a piece broken right out of the table. Whilst obviously this is not desirable, it may still be worth a further look. It is usually caused through over-tightening of the bolts holding the work which has not been properly sited in the first place, and the result is that the tee slot has been torn out. If the rest of the table shows no misuse, then the machine could be quite sound and at a later date it may be possible to machine out the broken part of the table and insert a mild steel section and machine this flat with the rest of the surface of the table to repair it.

Always try to see the machine running. Check where possible for spindle alignment and make sure that it runs true. Slackness in the table movement can usually be taken up by adjustment of the gib strips. If the table has a power feed, then ask to see it running as well. Strangely enough, milling machines do not seem to suffer from the same problems as lathes and most second-hand ones are in reasonable condition. Once I did find one where the spindle taper was worn away—how it had happened I worked out later, but that is not important. It is not the sort of area one normally checks, but it may well be worth while doing so. Finally, check that the machine is of the correct voltage. Also, many industrial machines are designed for three-phase electricity and unless your workshop is fitted with this, expense and trouble will be involved either getting the correct mains or changing the motor on the machine.

Second-hand machines can be obtained either direct from the owner or via dealers. They sometimes come up at auctions but frequently they do not go as cheaply as one would expect them to. Many suppliers of new machines take others in part exchange and will often let them go at a reasonable price just to clear floor space.

Having dealt with the basic machine, what then of desirable extras? Resettable indexing collars are to my mind most important. If the collars cannot be reset, then measurements have to be either remembered or recorded and this is much more difficult than just setting the dial to zero. A power feed on the table can be a useful feature. It will provide steady travel of the work which will give a better finish than operating the machine by hand. It is sometimes also possible to get a power down feed which can be used for drilling rows of holes, etc, as well as for boring. If some form of stop is available on the table travel, so much the better. If not, then fitting one is always worth doing. Some form of stand is desirable and if possible this should have facilities to catch and drain cutting fluids. It is also useful if the table has a well for this purpose.

Many other features you might like to look for will become apparent as you read on, we leave buying consideration for the time being. Buying a machine must be for the individual, but it may not do any harm to take along someone with a little more experience to help. Like so many other things it is usually a case of 'you get what you pay for' although there can be variations of quality within the same price range.

3 *USING THE LATHE AS A MILLING MACHINE*

For many years the lathe was the all-purpose machine for the vast majority of model engineers. Although very many home workshops now have milling machines of one sort or another, the lathe is still used quite extensively for milling.

Most model engineers of fifty years or more ago fitted out their workshops with an overhead shaft on which pulleys were used to drive machinery including, more often than not, the lathe itself. This practice was not surprising, as a visit to most engineering works right up to about 1938 would have shown a building with a series of shafts across the roof carrying several pulleys, each driving via a belt various types of machine. There would be one prime mover, possibly a petrol motor or steam engine, which drove the shafts and therefore, in effect, every machine in the factory.

It was on this basis that the model engineer worked, so milling attachments for the lathe developed along these lines. If a spindle was put on a column with vertical movement and driven from the overhead shaft, the lathe saddle — capable of being moved in either direction — could be used as a compound table and a form of milling machine was then available. The system was and is quite effective. I say 'is' because quite a few model engineers still use this idea although these days such spindles may well be driven independently by small electric motors. If one looks at the system logically there is no difference between this and the vertical milling machine.

The same applies to milling attachments specially designed for use with a lathe. These consist as a rule of bolt-on columns with vertical movement and independent motors. Many act as drilling machines as well as milling machines. On smaller machines, sometimes a subsidiary table is bolted to the cross slide to give a greater area on which to secure work. Some have tilting heads and they make an ideal compromise for those with a small workshop and who cannot stretch to a milling machine itself.

The other means of milling with a lathe is to use what is known as a vertical slide. This consists of a small table with vertical movement which bolts to the cross slide of the lathe. By placing a

Typical milling spindles. **Above** *is the Potts type, made from castings, which has been popular for many years.* **Below** *is a particularly fine example of a home-made spindle which has been fabricated. It is of the type very popular with clockmakers. The advantage of using the lathe for milling when clockmaking is twofold. First the headstock can be used for dividing and thus a separate dividing head is not needed. Secondly, as the work is very light the lathe adaptation is sufficiently robust to cope with almost any operation. Components can be machined on the lathe and milled* in situ *which means they are very accurate indeed.*

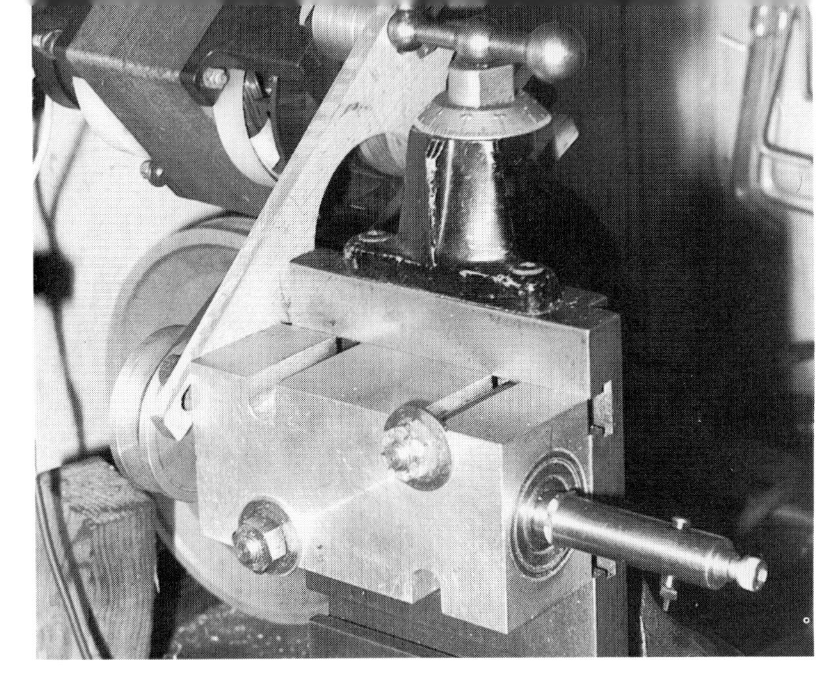

Above *A milling spindle in position on a vertical slide fixed to the lathe, and being used for clockmaking. Note the use of a single point home-made cutter for which this type of fitting is very suitable.*

Right *Most milling attachments have swivelling heads. Here we see one on a Harrison lathe set at an angle and being used for drilling. The advantage of the swivelling head is that the work itself need never be set at an angle.*

Below *A milling attachment fitted to a lathe. This bolts to the back of the lathe bed and the cross slide acts as the milling table.*

Harrison

Milling being carried out by using a cutter in the lathe chuck and with the work mounted on the cross slide, in this case using a small machine vice mounted, not on a vertical slide, but on an angle plate. The vertical slide would have to be used if a second, vertical, movement had been required. If this illustration is turned through 90 degrees it could easily be a photograph of work on a vertical milling machine. This means that apart from some loss of rigidity, there is little difference between working in this way on the lathe and using a vertical miller.

cutter in the mandrel either in the chuck or a collet the work can be bolted to the table of the vertical slide. This gives us a vertical milling machine working horizontally. The system is quite effective although it is necessary to use lighter cuts than on a milling machine because there is some loss of rigidity with the vertical slide.

Bearing in mind that all the systems of milling which use the lathe are in fact identical to a vertical milling machine, then all the advice given for using the vertical miller will apply equally to any form of milling with the lathe whether with the vertical slide or a special attachment.

4 *USING THE DRILLING MACHINE FOR MILLING*

The question often arises as to whether or not it is possible to use a drilling machine for milling. It is a somewhat awkward question to answer because it depends on so many factors, although it is probably fair to say that the majority of drilling machines could not be used successfully for this purpose. However, having said that, there are some that can be used and others that can be adapted. The actual operation of a drilling machine, with its up and down movement whilst rotating, is in many ways similar to that of the milling machine. All that has to be added is some form of horizontal movement.

A cross vice which can be used to convert a suitably strong drilling machine for milling.

A compound milling table designed to convert a drilling machine for use as a milling machine, or for use with a home-made spindle and column.

We can usually add the horizontal movement in two ways. The first, and in many ways the most successful, is to purchase what is known as a cross vice. This is a machine vice with a sub-frame and two handles, the rotation of which provide movement to the vice in two directions at right angles to each other. These vices come in various sizes to suit almost any size of drilling machine and they can be bolted to the drilling table. Most carry graduated scales on the handles and so are ideal for milling operations. If it is necessary to carry out operations on work that cannot be held in a vice, a sub-table can be made up which can then be gripped in the vice.

The second way to adapt a drilling machine is to fit it with a compound table. The compound table is the name given to the table on a milling machine but it is possible to purchase such tables separately at reasonable prices, or to purchase castings from which to make one's own. Some of the tables available are made in a form of aluminium which appears to be perfectly satisfactory and quite robust enough for most work.

If these accessories are available, then why should we hesitate to use them to convert any drilling machine to a milling machine? The answer to that lies in the construction of the drilling machine that is to be used. The first question to ask oneself is will it be up to the job? There are considerable forces involved in milling and much of the thrust is sideways. Most drilling machines have bearings designed only for a downward pressure, and in no time at all they would wear out if the thrust was sideways. So first of all ascertain the type of bearing. If the drilling machine has roller bearings which are very narrow, then it is unlikely they will withstand the pressure that is to be put on them. If, however, the bearings are wide and, even better, there is a double row of them, then in all probability they will come to no harm. Plain bronze bearings which are sometimes found on older drilling machines are often much more able to accept the sideways thrust than are the more modern ball bearings.

Secondly, what speeds will our drilling machine give us? If it has a wide choice then possibly it will do. You can check this with the tables in this book (Appendix 2). Down-feed can be a problem but this is not insurmountable because with most drilling machines it is possible to lock the downward movement with the stops. Remember, though, that with a machine not specifically designed for milling, the rule must be for only very light cuts to be taken.

We must also consider the diameter of the column, and whether or not it will stand the strain imposed on it and at the same time remain absolutely rigid. I think most drilling machines today have columns which are of adequate diameter.

The final question to be asked, and possibly the most important one of all, is what type of fitting does the machine have to hold the drilling chuck? Many have a male Jacobs taper. This is a very short and shallow taper and in no way will it accept the sideways thrust of milling—the chuck will just bounce out. One look at such a taper makes one realize that it will only take vertical thrust. If the chuck is fitted into a morse taper then it will not be unlike that of some milling machines, and there is every possibility that it will prove suitable. There is still a possibility of the taper coming out, though, unless the machine has a hollow mandrel with a fitted draw bar as with true milling machines.

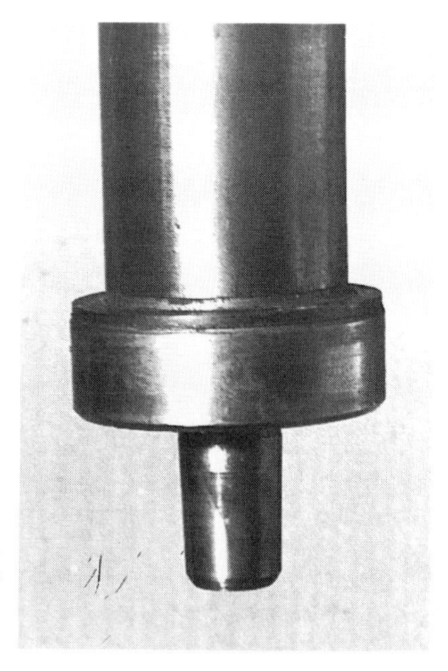

A male Jacobs taper. A drilling machine with this fitting would not be suitable for milling purposes.

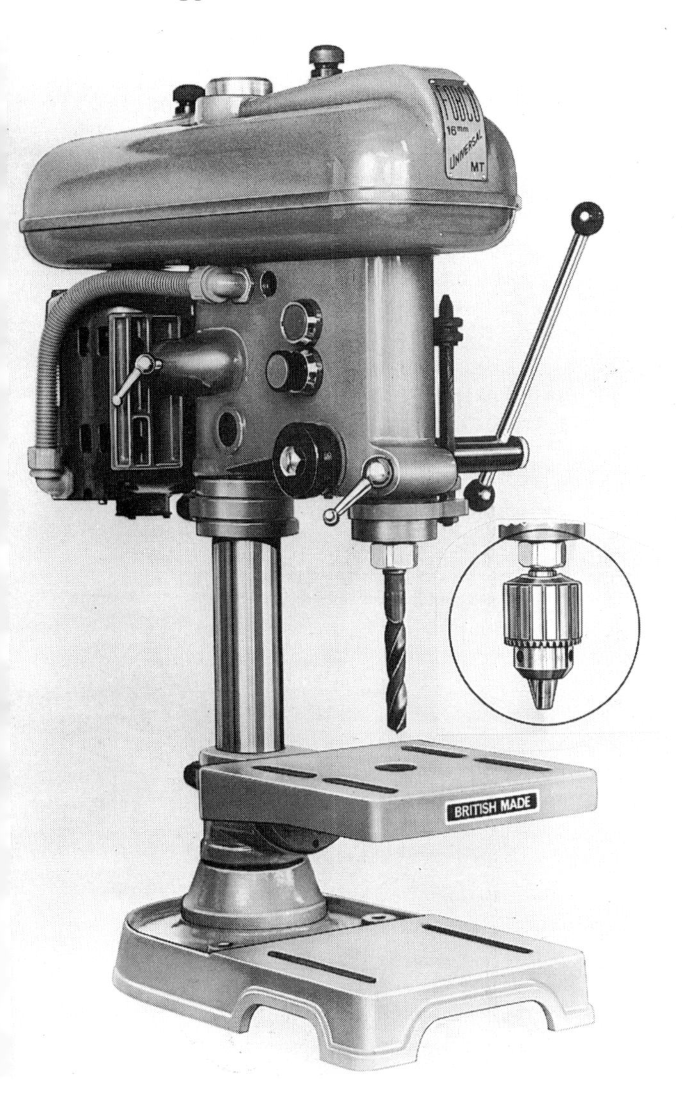

A drilling machine by Fobco specially constructed to be used also as a milling machine.

This brings us to the question of the chuck itself and whether or not it is capable of gripping a milling cutter securely whilst milling operations are carried out. If we look at a drill chuck there is not much bearing surface on the jaws, which are really designed to cope with a variety of diameters rather than clamp round one of a set size. Ask yourself if, during drilling operations when you have felt confident that the chuck was tight, the drill moved further into the chuck as drilling progressed. If the answer to that is 'yes', then it is unlikely that the drill chuck will hold a milling cutter firmly in position.

Given the fact that the drilling machine has a female taper and a hollow mandrel, there is no reason whatever why special collets should not be made up to accept set sizes of milling cutters

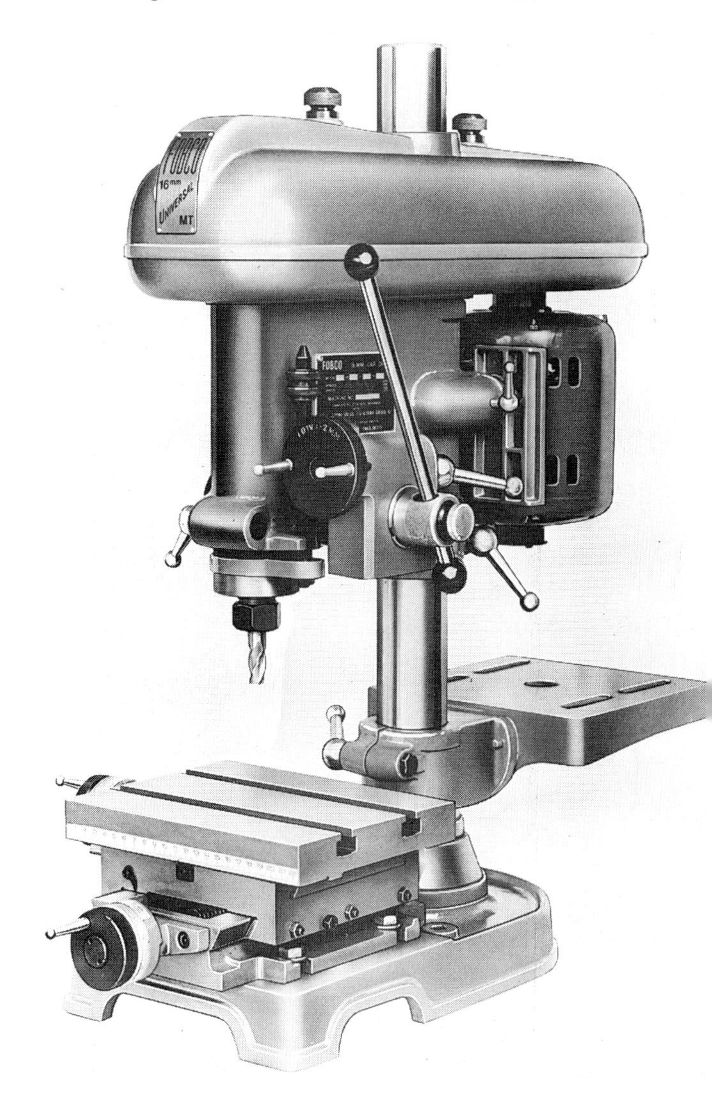

To convert the Fobco drill, a special milling table designed to fit on the base and suitable collets for holding cutters are available.

retained with grub screws, and drawn in tight with a draw bar. The effect would be the same as with the mandrel of a milling machine.

It is possible to purchase drilling machines which are designed to be used also as milling machines or to be converted to one. If purchasing a drill, it is worth seeing if one of this type can be obtained. The price difference is not great and the extra bearing strength well worth having.

Finally, let me say that if the drilling machine is to double for a miller, and for many it could well be 'Hobson's choice', then treat it carefully. Take much lighter cuts than would be expected from a proper milling machine, and do not feed too quickly. Nonetheless, many model engineers have no choice but to work in this way and they do so very successfully.

5 *SAFETY*

The question of safety in the workshop, whether concerning milling or any other operation, cannot be over-stressed. It is mainly a question of care and common sense, but there are some precautions which should be taken.

Dress is possibly the first thing to think about. Shoes for example—it may be very nice to wander into the workshop on a quiet Sunday morning, wearing a dressing gown and house slippers and idly start work. Possibly the mode of dress will inhibit one from actually working the machine, but then there is no harm in setting it up. But is there? If the large iron casting to be set up happens to slip and land on your foot only clad in a house slipper, the owner of that foot I am quite sure will be inclined to say 'bother!' At all times shoes must be worn in the workshop. In industry, heavy boots would be compulsory. In the home workshop there is admittedly no desire for a complete change of clothing every time one wants to indulge in a hobby, but shoes are a *must*, and if boots with heavy toecaps are used, so much the better. Heavy castings can really make one hop about if they fall on unprotected feet, and if only a cutter is dropped, then I am sure the reader knows which way up it will land on the foot.

Loose sleeves and long hair can be a problem as they have a nasty habit of catching in rotating machines. Sleeves can easily be prevented from flapping around by the use of a couple of elastic bands. If hair is cut short there will be no problem, otherwise a hat kept around the workshop will keep the hair in place. Wearing a cap or hat also prevents oils and swarf from getting into the hair and subsequently making a mess on the best pillow slips.

Safety glasses will prevent swarf from flying into the eyes. There is not a great deal involved in keeping a pair by the machine and slipping them on during operations and it could save damage to the eyes not only from swarf but possibly from cutting fluids splashing about. I do not wear them myself for setting up, although I supose I should, but experience has taught me that when the machine is actually in operation it is well worth putting them on.

There is a case for wearing a simple form of mask when using

Right *Wearing a hat and safety glasses will prevent the hair from catching in moving machinery and swarf or cutting fluid from splashing into the eyes.*

Below *A glove will protect the hand from injury if the spanner slips, and elastic bands on the wrist will stop sleeves catching in rotating tools.*

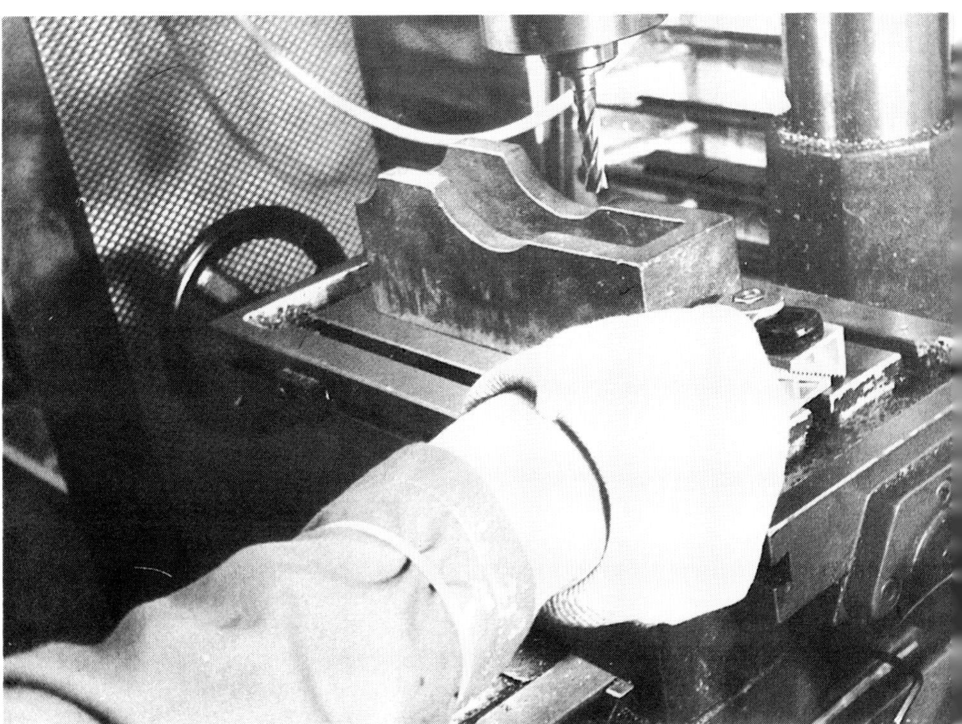

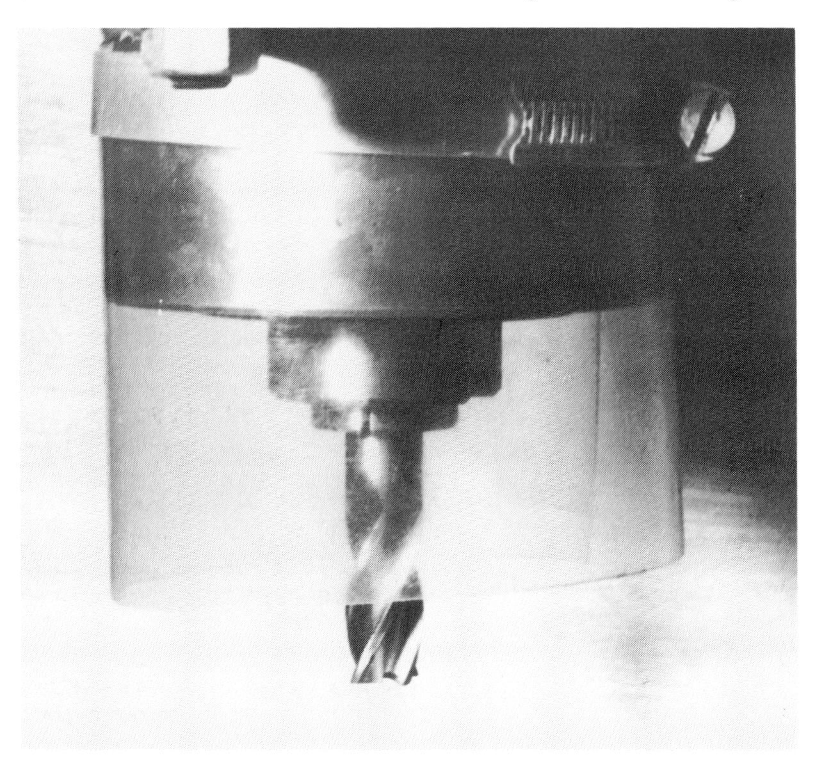

A home-made cutter guard using a piece of perspex held in place with a hose clip. The guard will prevent hands from accidently touching the moving cutter. It also helps to prevent swarf and cutting oil from flying about.

cutting fluids, or machining cast iron, both of which can irritate the throat, and there is also a case for wearing an overall which will protect one from splashes of cutting fluids which can be irritants to the skin. If the work in hand makes it essential for it to be flooded with cutting lubricant, a plastic apron will prevent most of it from getting on clothes. It is easier to wipe it off the apron than to wash out clothes or overalls.

All this is not to suggest that one should spend precious leisure time dressed as an out-of-work spaceman. Protective clothing need only be worn as required for a particular operation, and during setting up periods more casual dress would not cause any great harm. This is not, of course, an opinion we are likely to get from a factory inspector, but after all it is a hobby.

So far it would seem that safety is only concerned with dress, but this is far from true. Simple precautions in the workshop with equipment can save nasty cuts and bruises, or even more serious injury. For example, when tightening nuts or bolts make sure the spanner you are using is the correct size for the nut and unlikely to slip. Also it is worth wearing gloves for the operation as these can prevent cuts on the hand in the event of a mishap. I keep a pair of gardening gloves in the workshop and slip them on for such work. In theory I suppose gloves should be worn to avoid splinters in the hands, but they are not necessarily the best thing for continuous wear since splinters can find their way into the gloves thus irritating the hands through the material and causing quite painful little abrasions. So perhaps the best course of action is to wear them when it seems most likely that harm might otherwise be done.

Before changing cutters, etc, to prevent it accidentally being switched on all machinery should be switched off at the mains. All loose articles should also be removed from the machine to prevent them being knocked off and damaged or causing injury.

Any oil or other liquid spillages on the floor should be cleared up as soon as possible to prevent slipping.

Put all tools, etc, away after use. A tidy workshop is a safe workshop. This also applies to metal—do not leave odd lengths or pieces laying around. Put away in your store what is not required for immediate use.

Make sure there is good ventilation in the workshop to prevent a build-up of fumes from cutting oils, coolants, etc, and always have some form of good fire extinguisher, or a blanket, available just in case.

It all sounds somewhat frightening and might make one wonder if the hobby is worthwhile. It is not as bad as all that, however, and these precautions are really simple common sense, most of which make for a cleaner and tidier workshop, as well as a safe one. I have refrained from giving a complete breakdown of the various safety measures which are compulsory in industry. Perhaps I should have done, but personally I feel that such regulations if carried out exhaustively in the home workshop would make the hobby unbearable and I hope I have set out a sensible compromise. I know that much of what I have written will not be acted on by some readers, and others will use all the precautions I have suggested and possibly others. That is a matter for the individual. When it is analysed, the most important safety precaution is one's own attitude. If a person is sensible then normally they will be safe and so it is this attitude that we must develop.

6 *PLANNING AND PREPARING THE JOB*

When milling operations are to be carried out, planning and preparation are important factors, and it is worthwhile developing a method or sequence of operations. To start at once on the work without any form of planning is courting disaster, and so often if mistakes are made they are either extremely expensive to rectify, or cannot be rectified at all. The following are some suggestions that might avoid such pitfalls.

First study the drawing very carefully so as to be thoroughly familiar with what you are going to do. Work out your sequence of operations and if need be make notes of the way you intend to carry out the work. Try and organize things so that as few settings of the work as possible are required. For example, can the work be clamped in such a way that two or even three faces can be milled at the one setting?

Check the material or casting and ensure that there is sufficient machining allowance; see also how the best use can be made of that allowance. If a casting, then check for possible blow holes and faults. There is no point in spending hours machining a casting and then having to replace it and start all over again. Decide what clamps or vice will be needed and set these to one side ready for use. It is essential that the workpiece should always be held very firmly; use the simplest possible method of holding that is consistent with this.

Select the cutters that will be required and have the measuring tools ready. It is no good halfway through the job having to search the workshop for a certain tool; it should be on hand.

Check that the work is correctly set, particularly as regards squareness, and then check the safety precautions that are necessary. Set the correct cutter speed and finally make a dummy run along and near the work with the cutter rotating at the required speed. This gives one the feel of the work (rather like a golfer with a practice swing) and it is surprising how errors can be found in this way. It is very much better to discover such errors before the cutter has made contact with the metal.

7 *HOLDING CUTTERS DURING MILLING OPERATIONS*

It will be stressed time and time again throughout this book that rigidity is essential for good milling. Without this there will be both inaccuracies and bad finishing. This rigidity applies not only when holding work for operations to be carried out but also in retaining cutters.

In the case of horizontal machines, the cutter is held between spacers or collars on the mandrel and the security of the cutter will depend on these spacers being correctly set. They are tightened by means of a nut at the end of the mandrel and on the vast majority of machines the thread is long enough to take up any discrepancies in collar sizes. The collars come in a variety of widths to allow the correct position of the cutter to be found. The only real need then is to ensure that the securing nut is tight, and the cutter secure on the key which in turn is in the keyway. Then, providing nothing silly has been done like not putting in enough spacers, there is little more to worry about.

Whilst the cutter is usually prevented from rotating on the shaft by a key which obviously helps security, there are one or two machines which rely purely on the pressure applied by the nut. But these are not often encountered and anyway, surprisingly enough, sufficient torque can be obtained to prevent the cutter remaining stationary on the revolving mandrel, just on pressure alone. Some slitting saws are constructed without provision for keying and this does not in any way seem to impair their efficiency.

The only other thing to watch out for with the horizontal machine is that the cutter is located on the mandrel as centrally as possible. It is very bad practice and likely to cause vibration if it is not. Like most of our model engineering, it is really a matter of common sense.

When it comes to the vertical milling machine, the arrangements for cutter holding are much more diverse. We must, I think, first of all find out the type of mandrel on the machine before we can discuss methods of cutter holding. Almost all vertical milling machines have a taper in the nose or mandrel. The types of taper vary, a fairly common one being the morse taper which is also

A milling arbor, spacers and some milling cutters. The arbor is located in the machine by the taper and the cutter mounted on it with spacers on either side. They are secured in place with a key and a nut at the end furthest from the taper.

Using a dividing head on the horizontal milling machine. Note how the support bearing has been moved in towards the cutter and spacers put on the outside of it. This sort of set-up gives greater rigidity to the cutter.

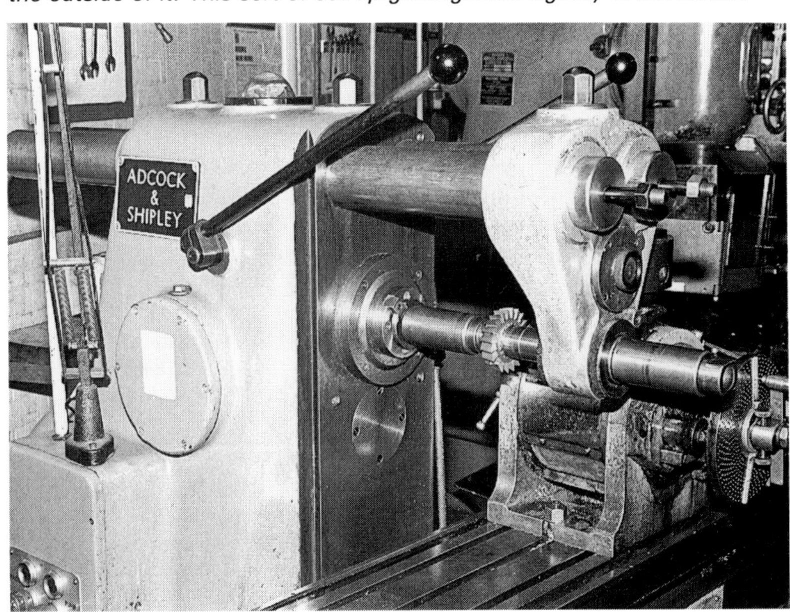

The Fastlock chuck, a patient collet chuck for screwed end mills, and the best way of holding cutters in position.

The two threaded end mills (below) are designed to screw into a collet chuck, but they will work perfectly well in split collets. Above them is a slot drill with a morse taper, designed to fit directly into a morse taper sleeve without a draw bar.

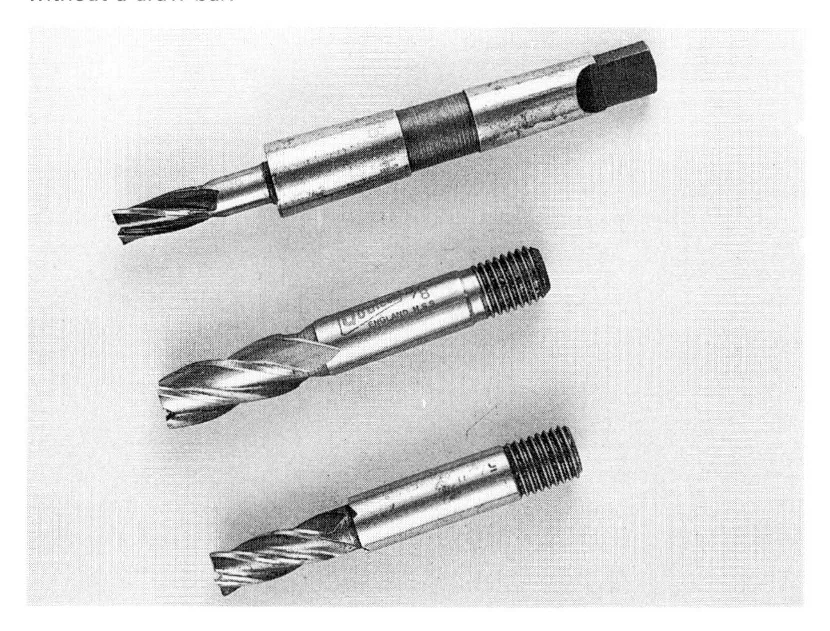

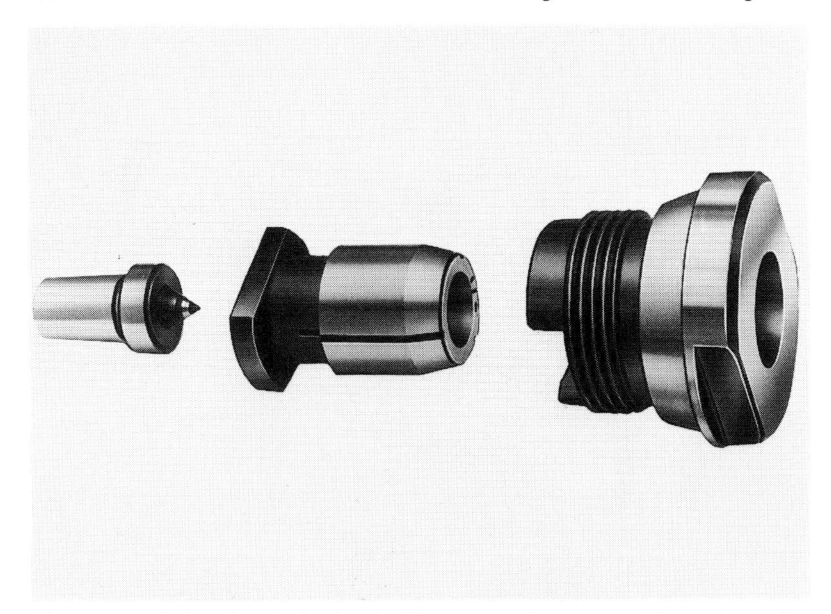

The parts of the Fastlock chuck. The cutter is screwed into the collet (centre) which mates with the centre in the component on the left and ensures absolute accuracy. The cap (right) is screwed home to keep everything tight.

usually found in lathes. Having the same taper on the milling machine as in one's lathe is very useful as it allow interchangeability between tooling. Morse tapers come in a variety of sizes and the size will depend largely on the size of the machine. There are at least two other types of taper likely to be found on milling machines. One is known as an R8 and this differs from the morse variety in that it has quite a sharp taper at the end and a much shallower one further along. The other type is known as the 'international'. It is similar to the morse but of a much steeper angle. The reason for the use of these two types of taper is possibly to save some length in the mandrel because, having steeper angles, they are not as long as the morse taper. All three types are quite suitable and their principle is fairly simple, relying on the mating surfaces to obtain a grip and at the same time to provide accuracy.

To ensure that the tapers are pulled right home it is usual to have a draw bar. This is a piece of threaded rod with a hexagon or similar section at one end. The draw bar goes right through the axis of the mandrel and locates in a thread in the end of the appliance being used. When tightened up, it draws the male taper tightly home into the female taper of the machine. In fact, when the draw bar is loosened it will probably require a smart tap on the top end with a hide mallet to release the tapers. Some of the milling attachments do not have a draw bar fitting and we will come to these later. The draw bar will certainly give a great deal of added security to tool holding.

Having dealt with that, we must now think about the actual cutter and how it is secured and without any doubt the best way is to use a correctly designed collet holder. These are available under a variety of brand names but the principle is the same in all cases.

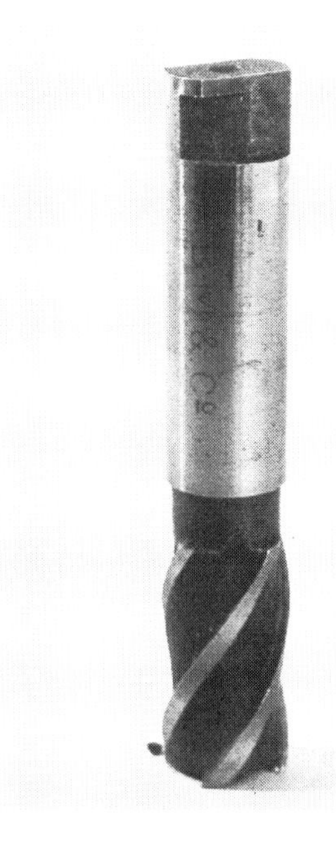

Right *An HSCO flatted shank end mill designed to fit into a patent collet of a type not frequently seen these days. It will, however, fit into a split collet quite well.*

Below *A set of split collets with a nose cap for tightening.*

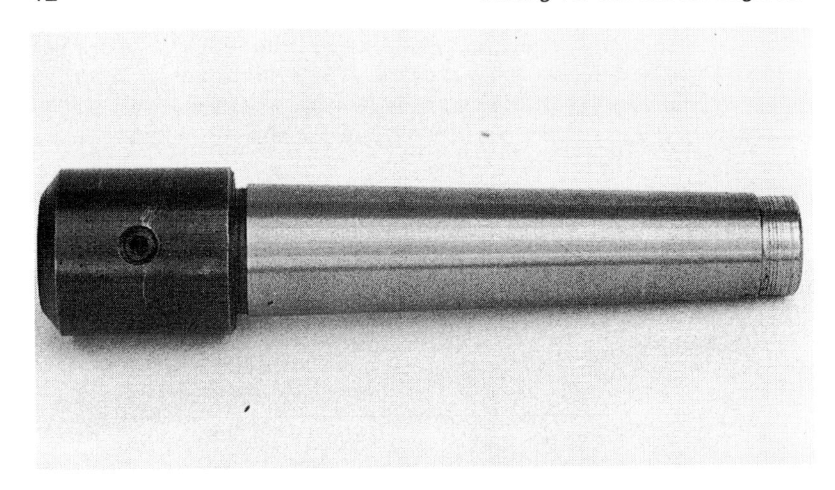

Top *A morse taper collet designed to be held in the machine with a draw bar. The cutter is held in with a grub screw. When using this type of collet, a flat must be ground on the cutter to accept the screw.*

Above *A split morse taper collet designed for use with a draw bar. This will accept almost any cutter of the correct diameter.*

The main holder body has a taper threaded through its centre to accept a draw bar. The other end is threaded to accept a nose cap which, when tightened, will ensure rigidity of the cutter. Into this nose piece fits a collet with possibly a guide as well. The cutter screws into the collet and there is a centre in the main body of the chuck which ensures concentricity by locating with the centre hole in the cutter. All cutters are threaded 20 threads per inch (or 1mm pitch if metric). It is useful to know this because if we are going to make cutters at any time then the screw thread of this pitch will have to be machined on it if this type of collet holder is in use.

Split collets may also be used. These are made to the same taper as the machine each with a set size of hole, and they will accept cutters of the same set size. When a split collet is used the cutter is inserted and the collet is tightened up by the draw bar. This will clamp it round the cutter thus holding it rigid. This system is not as good as the collet chuck described above as, under extreme pressure, it is possible for the cutter to slip in the collet, which cannot happen with a collet chuck.

A third method of securing the cutter again uses a collet held in place by a draw bar. In this case, however, the cutter is first put in the collet and rotation prevented by tightening up a grub screw. This method is quite effective but it is necessary to ensure that the grub screw is properly tightened up to prevent the cutter from rotating independently. For these collets special cutters are made on which small flats have been ground to provide a surface for the grub screw to grip. Ordinary threaded cutters could be used although a flat should then be ground on the shank to allow the grub screw to locate.

There is no doubt that the collet chuck, the first method described, is the most efficient but it is also by far the most expensive. For most model engineering needs either of the other two methods will prove satisfactory. However, the situation may arise where the machine has a taper larger than some of the tools or collets to be used. In this case an adapter sleeve can be obtained which will allow the smaller equipment to fit the larger taper. Some such adapters have a threaded collar which is an aid to ejecting the tool from the adapter, and in turn the adapter from the machine. Whilst adapters are useful, there is almost bound to be some loss of accuracy and rigidity in use and so, if possible, the correct sized taper should be used, although adapters can save a considerable amount of expense.

In the case of a milling attachment, sometimes no draw bar is provided and then the cutter will have to rely entirely on friction to

A morse taper adapter. This will enable a small morse taper to fit into a larger one. It is a self-releasing adapter because the large nut may be wound in either direction to force the adapter from the tapers. If it is necessary to use a taper adapter, this one is more rigid than the normal type supplied for drilling machines and it also will accept the milling machine draw bar.

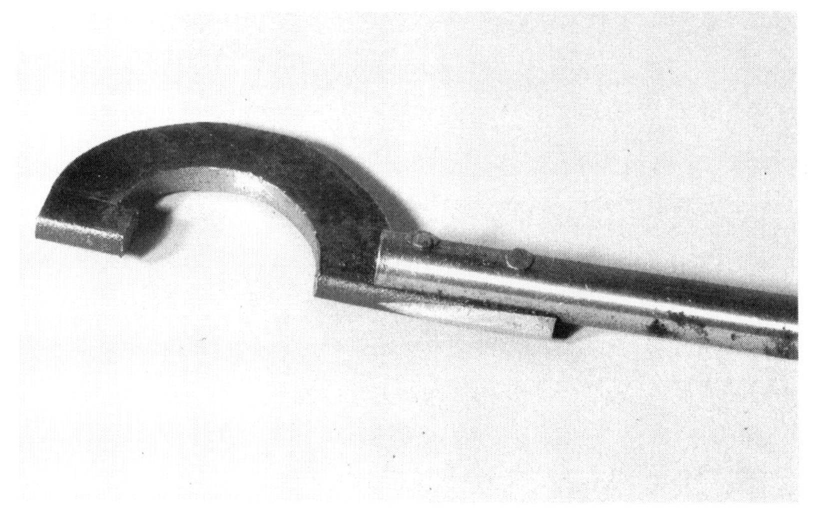

Top *The nose of a milling machine mandrel. The two slots, one at each side, are designed to lock specially designed tools in position. They can also be used to great advantage for holding the mandrel still while tightening up a draw bar. A 'C' spanner is used in one slot and held against the rotation caused by the operation of unscrewing the draw bar.* **Above** *A 'C' spanner made to fit the end of a milling machine mandrel.*

hold it in position. Usually in such cases there will be a morse taper and, providing the work being carried out is not too heavy, this will do the work. It is a far from satisfactory arrangement, but there is little to be done about it if that is how the machine is made. Some manufacturers suggest the use of a drilling machine with a compound table for milling, but, as explained in Chapter 4, the use of a drill chuck for holding milling cutters is not an idea to be encouraged as the type of construction means that the jaws only bear on a small part of the cutter, whereas with a collet the whole of the circumference is supported. If money is a problem, then it may be 'Hobson's choice', but if so every care must be taken when milling to only take very light cuts.

Apart from milling cutters, other tools such as fly cutters and slitting saws may also be used in a milling machine. The fly cutter should preferably be fitted with a matching taper to that of the machine and held with a draw bar. Holding a straight-shanked fly cutter in a collet will work and, again, if cuts are not too heavy, no harm will come to it. The pressure is, however, continually being applied to one side of the collet which cannot be a good thing, and a secure taper fitting is far more efficient. Slitting saws are held on a mandrel which may have either a taper shank secured with a draw bar or it can have a straight shank and be held in a collet as in that case the forces are applied evenly all round. If the mandrel is made with a straight shank it is best if it is threaded and held in the collet chuck. Should this not prove possible for reasons of cost, then the second choice should be a collet and grub screw arrangement, with the split collet, whilst still satisfactory, being third in line. In any case the shank of the saw mandrel should be made as large a diameter as possible as this provides a greater area to take the forces involved.

Cutters should always be held as deep as possible within collets.

A home-made mandrel for holding slitting saws. It consists of a simple stepped bar and a large washer. The washer secures the slitting saw in position with a screw.

Top *A more complicated mandrel, and probably more efficient, for holding slitting saws. It is commercially made and a clever spring device allows saws of different bores to be held.*

Above *The parts of the commercial slitting saw mandrel. All the steps slip out of the way when the saw is mounted, leaving it on the one of the right diameter and of exactly the correct width.*

In the case of the collet chuck, the correct depth is obtained by means of the thread but in other cases care must be taken to push the cutter right home. If milling is being carried out for any length of time using the same cutter, it is advisable to check the draw bar occasionally and ensure tightness during operations as it is not impossible for cutters to work loose.

Whilst some knowledge of the types of fixings in use is of assistance, choice will invariably be limited to the fitting relevant to the individual machine. However, common sense is the important thing as it is in so many cases. It must be remembered that in milling considerable force is being applied and it is essential that everything possible is done to ensure that cutters are secured sufficiently to accept the amount of force applied. A good idea is to take a piece of mild steel, say $\frac{1}{2}$ in, or 12 mm, thick and some 2 in or 50 mm long. File about $\frac{1}{8}$ in, or 3 mm, off it without a break and see how tired you are! It may take as much as an hour, but your milling machine will do it in 10 minutes, which means it is using probably six times the force you expended. That should make you realize why care must be taken to secure cutters properly.

Whatever type of collet is used, it is worth having a knowledge of the sizes generally available which are suitable for the model engineer. Imperial sizes are $\frac{1}{4}$, $\frac{3}{8}$, $\frac{1}{2}$, $\frac{5}{8}$ and $\frac{3}{4}$ in (or 6, 10, 12, 16 and 20 mm if using metric measurements).

8 *CUTTERS FOR HORIZONTAL MILLING MACHINES*

It is fairly obvious that the horizontal milling machine uses different types of cutters from the vertical machine, although the principle is the same. For the quick removal of metal using a horizontal miller, a slab cutter is used. This is rather like a roller with cutting teeth arranged in a spiral form around the periphery. It is also sometimes referred to as a plain cutter, and with no cutting edges on the sides, it follows that it can only be used for generating a flat surface. Slab cutters can be obtained in a variety of sizes, but the centre hole will have to conform with the mandrel, although different-sized mandrels for the machine can be obtained or made. There is also a square recess in the centre of the cutter to take a key to prevent the cutter turning on the mandrel.

A slab cutter. This is a massive cutter designed for rapid machining of flat surfaces. Some idea of the size can be gauged from the central hole and keyway. When using slab cutters they should, if possible, extend over the width of the surface to be machined. There are no side teeth and the cutter can only be used for this single purpose.

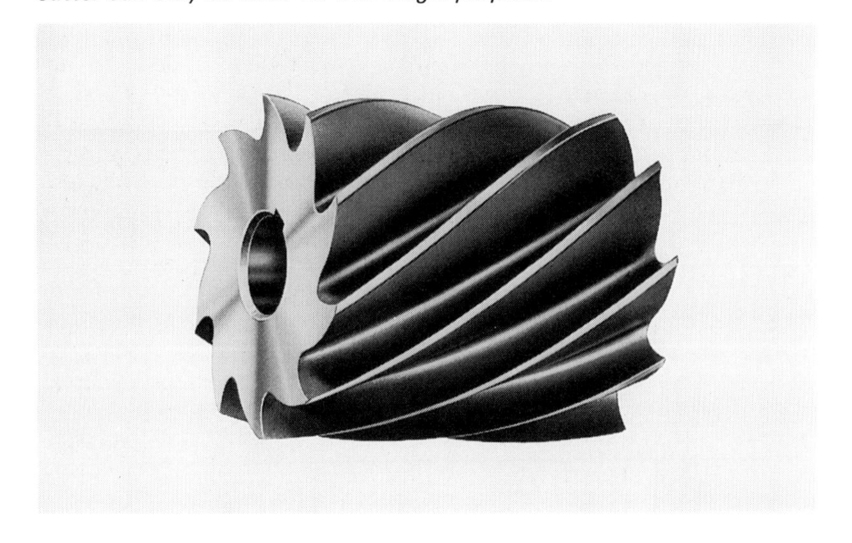

A side and face cutter used for cutting the edges of material as well as flat surfaces. It can also be used for grooving. The picture clearly shows the large central hole and the keyway used to secure the cutter to the machine mandrel.

The side and face cutter, as its name implies, will cut either around the periphery or along the edges of the work. It can therefore be used for cutting slots and recesses as well as generating flat planes. It is also possible to obtain slotting cutters which cut on the face only and which are narrow enough and which have sufficient side clearance to allow their use for slot cutting. Similar cutters are available with either angled or radiused teeth which allow the cutting of convex, concave or angled surfaces. It is fairly obvious what use each could be put to since all these shaped cutters have teeth designed for a particular job and they are not really adaptable for other purposes.

Slitting saws are very narrow circular saws which can be obtained in a variety of diameters and widths as well as various tooth formations. They can be used for actually cutting through a metal section, for cutting recesses or for making very fine slots. They are very efficient and whatever type of milling machine you are using it is always worth having one or two slitting saws in stock. The same type of slitting saw is also used on a vertical

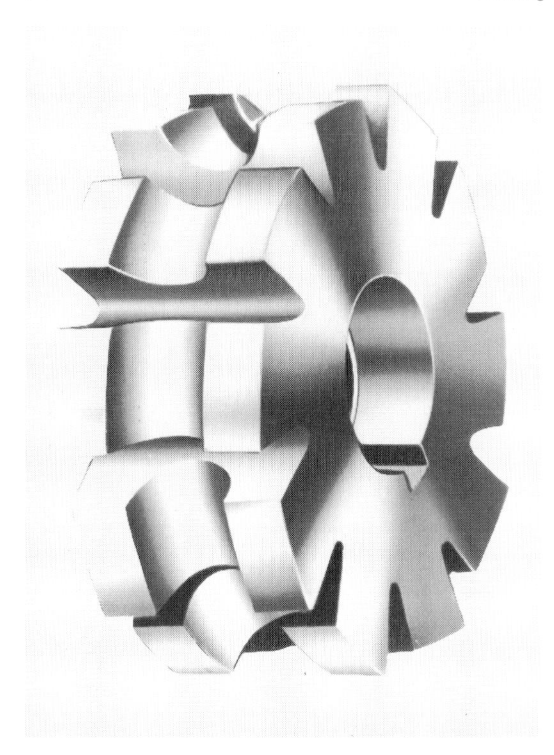

A concave cutter. The shape of the cutter speaks for itself.

A convex cutter. Both this and the concave cutter are useful for forming shapes particularly along the edges of material.

milling machine when it is held in an arbor.

It is possible to make single point cutters to particular profiles for use on the horizontal machine. These are rather like fly cutters, and consist of a piece of round bar with a hole through the centre to allow it to fit over the mandrel of the machine. A single cutting tool is inserted into a hole in the side of the bar and locked in position with a grub screw. Each pass over the metal as it rotates makes a small cut and therefore feeding the cutter along the work can be a slow process. Such cutters are useful however when cutting recesses and they can be made up in gangs of three for milling the ports for slide valves on steam engines.

Cutters for horizontal milling machines are expensive and so when they become blunt it is well worth taking them to a specialist engineering firm for sharpening, because unless special machines are available it is not possible to sharpen them in the home workshop. This does not of course apply to the home-made single point cutter which can be sharpened on a bench grinder.

9 *CUTTERS FOR VERTICAL MILLING MACHINES*

The first type of cutter one thinks of for the vertical milling machine is an end mill. These usually have four flutes but otherwise are not unlike a flat-ended drill bit. Both the end and the sides can be used for cutting purposes, and they can be obtained to a standard length as well as in long and extra long series. End mill diameters are generally stocked in imperial sizes in stages of $\frac{1}{32}$ in, although the odd $\frac{1}{64}$ can be obtained to special order. In metric sizes they are available in 1 mm stages up to 8 mm and 2 mm stages thereafter. The larger diameters are particularly useful for milling along the edge of work using the side of the cutter.

Shell end mills are mainly of larger diameter than ordinary end mills. They have more cutting flutes, the number depending to some degree on the diameter of the cutter. These cutters have to be mounted on an arbor for use. The sides are not as long as the

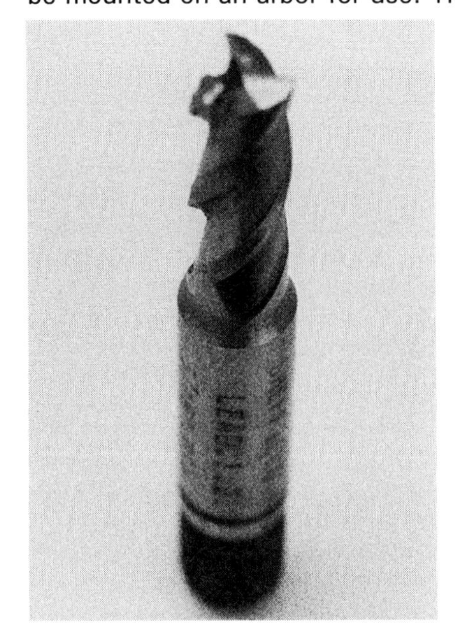

A three-fluted cutter.

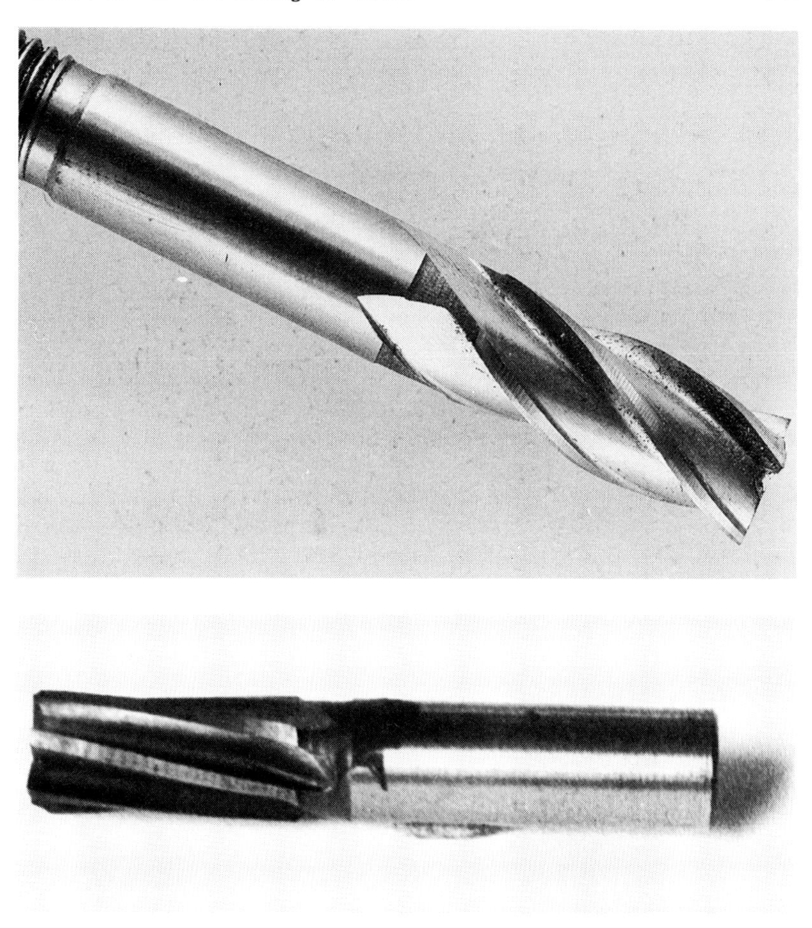

Top *A standard end mill with screwed shank.*

Above *A somewhat unusual six-fluted cutter. A splodge of paint can be seen just above the teeth on the shank denoting that it is not to be used until sharpened on any metal except steel.*

sides of end mills and they are not normally used for milling purposes, work just being carried out with the face. A more recent development in this type of cutter has been to manufacture them with removable carbide inserts. This saves the necessity of sharpening and also means that higher milling speeds may be used.

Slot drills come with either two or three cutting edges, two being the more normal. They have one cutting edge slightly shorter than the other and can be plunged into work like a drill which cannot be done with an end mill. As the name implies they are mainly intended for cutting slots, the wider flute obtained by the lower number of cutting edges giving good clearances for this type of work. A word of warning here, though. If cutting a slot to the full diameter of the slot drill, do not be tempted to wind back the milling machine with the cutter still rotating, since this will result in an

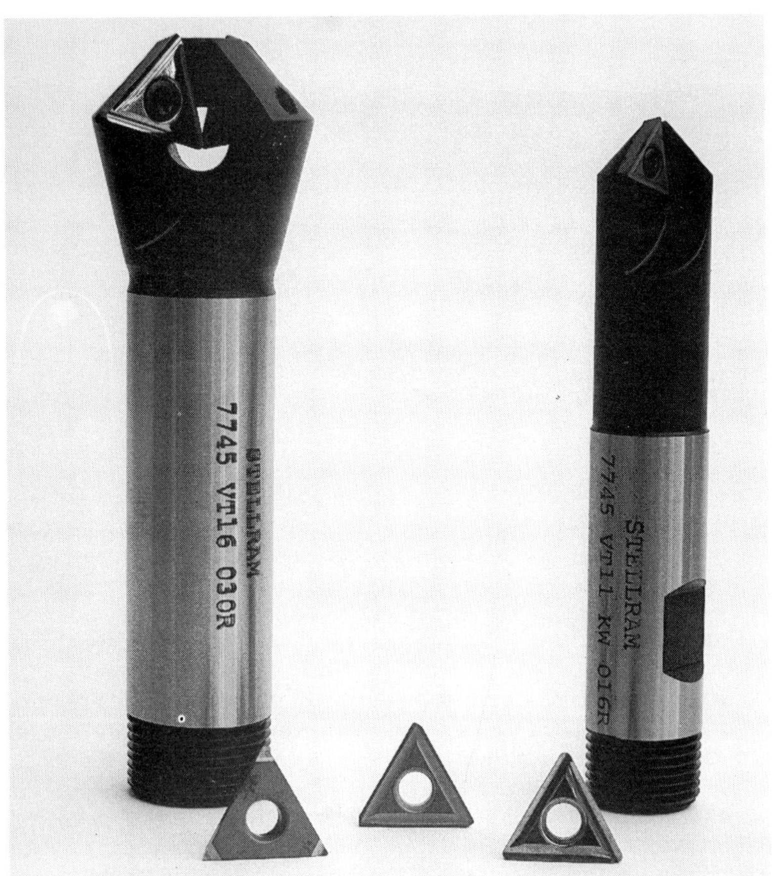
STELLRAM
7745 VT16 030R
STELLRAM
7745 VT11 KW 016R

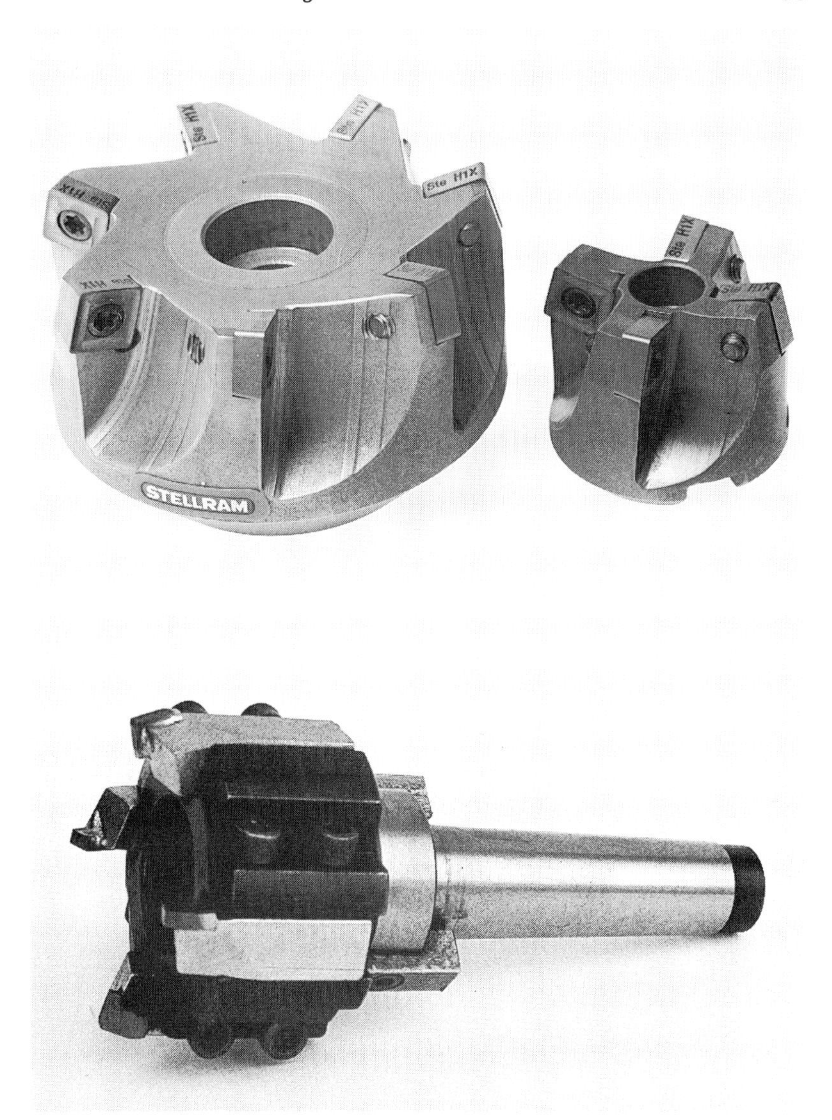

Top left *A shell end mill, designed for the removal of large areas of metal, has to be used on a special mandrel. This type of cutter has been largely superceded by the multi-point tipped type.*

Left *Two examples of cutters with removable carbide tips. The cutters shown are designed for chamfering.*

Top *Two multi-point cutters with removable carbide tips. As can be seen, these tips can be replaced by new ones held in place by small grub screws.*

Above *A different type of multi-tipped cutter. In this case the tips are brazed to holders and are designed to be resharpened when blunt. No special equipment is needed for resharpening other than a green grit grindstone.*

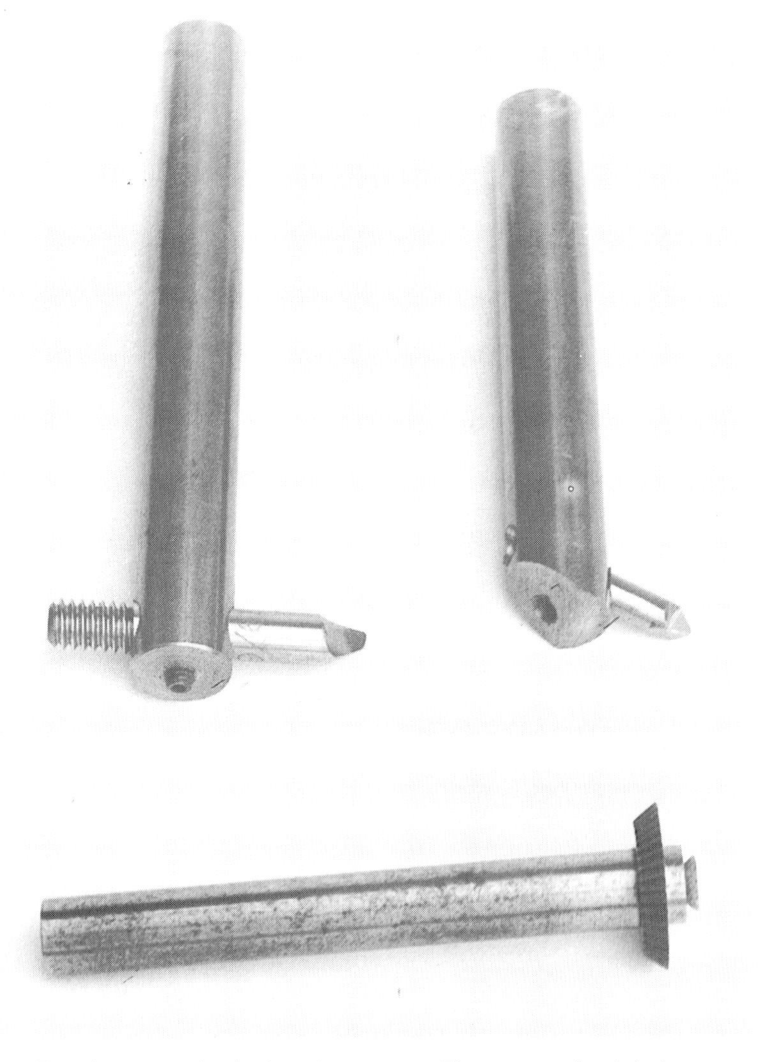

Top *Two home-made single point cutters. The one on the right is more or less a small fly cutter and can be used for general work at quite high speeds. That on the left has been designed to cut a gear wheel, and has been ground from a broken end mill.*

Above *Many different and specially shaped cutters can be obtained for gear cutting, particularly for cutting clock gears.*

oversized slot. The cutter should always be withdrawn first. One particular advantage of a slot drill for the home machinist is that because it only has two cutting edges it can be touched up on a grindstone when it becomes blunt. The slot drill will still function perfectly well if only one edge is cutting as it then works rather on the principle of a fly cutter. Like end mills they can be obtained in

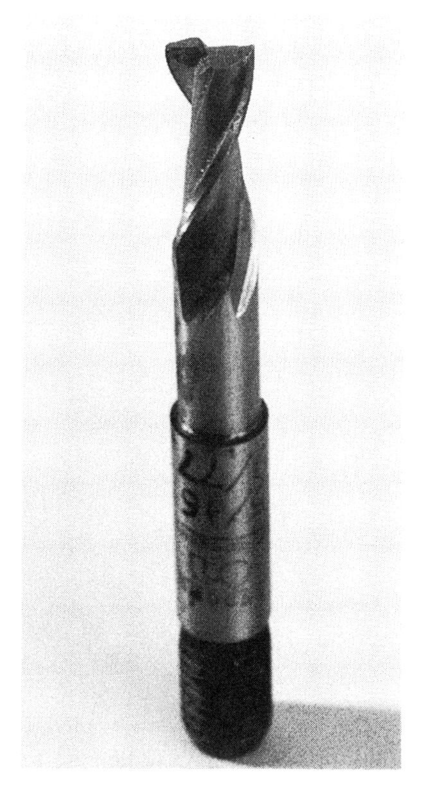

A slot drill with a screwed shank to fit into the chuck of a vertical milling machine.

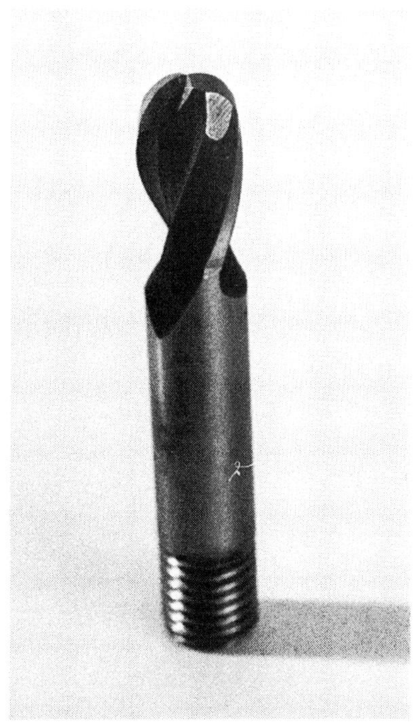

A ball-nosed end mill.

A woodruff key cutter. This type of cutter is designed to be plunged into a shaft to make a semicircular space for a woodruff key. However, they work quite well as small slot cutters.

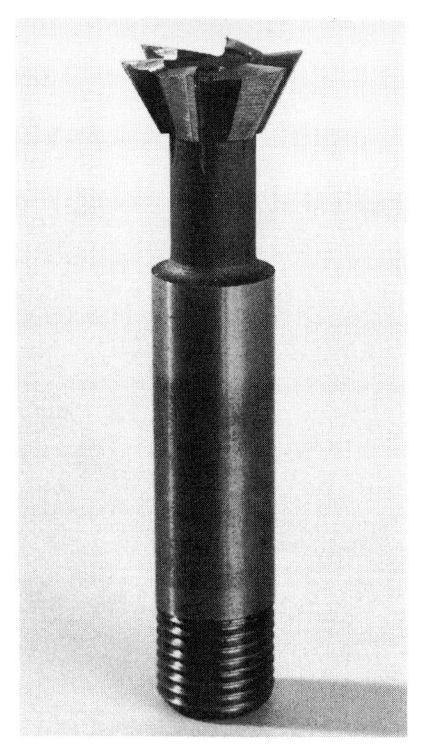

A dovetail cutter.

Right *A tee slot cutter. Note that the shank is cut back to allow plenty of clearance when cutting a tee slot.*

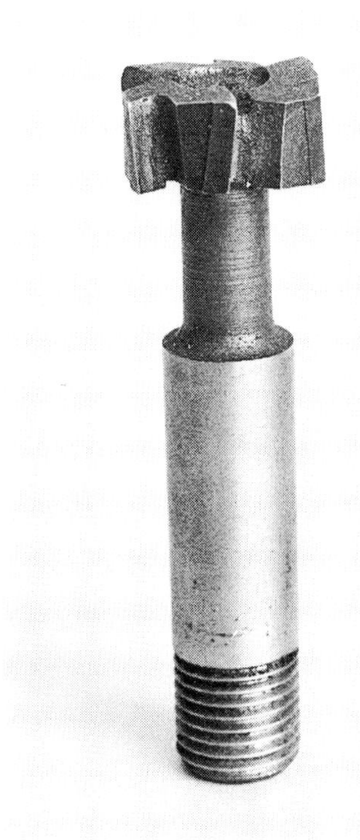

Below *A slitting or slotting saw. These can be obtained in a variety of thicknesses and diameters, as well as with different teeth patterns. They are extremely useful and one or two are always worth having to hand.*

A typical fly cutter, a tool easily made at home which will give a beautiful finish if traversed slowly at low speed. Whenever possible the cutter should completely cover in one sweep the surface being machined.

three lengths and to a similar range of diameters.

The three flute type of slot drill is really a cross between an end mill and a slot drill, and it can be used in either form. The cutter was originally specially developed for high-speed production work although it is now generally available to the model engineer.

Ball-ended and concave cutters are simply end mills with rounded ends. They are available for particular purposes when a radius is required.

The dovetail cutter is used, as the name implies, for cutting dovetails and comes in angles of 30, 45 and 60 degrees. It is especially useful when making workshop equipment.

The woodruff key cutter is used for making slots for woodruff keys and is designed to be plunged directly into the work to form the typical half round recess of the woodruff key. They can, however, be used for cutting keyways, etc. They are also very useful for cutting flutes in the coupling rods and connecting rods of model locomotives.

The tee slot cutter is similar to the woodruff cutters but frequently the shank has a smaller diameter just above the cutter itself to allow it to be run along a slot previously made with a slot drill. As the name implies, it is used for making tee slots, but like the woodruff cutter it can also be used for fluting, etc.

Slitting saws have been described in the chapter on cutters for horizontal machines. They can be used on vertical machines with a suitable arbor and, generally, are highly efficient.

Fly cutters are single point tools which many model engineers make for themselves. They consist of a ground tool bit arranged to swing off centre giving a comparatively wide radius to the cut. Usually a very nice finish may be obtained, but because of their very nature they are slower to operate than most other types of cutter. However, they do have the advantage of being easily sharpened in the home workshop and are cheap to make. Some that are purchased, and no doubt some home-made ones as well, employ a replacable carbide cutting edge and this will allow work to be carried out faster than is normal with the usual high-speed tool. When using a fly cutter, the aim should always be to use one that will give a wider sweep than the surface being machined, so that the operation can be carried out in one pass. This may not always be possible but it is almost certain that, in making more than one pass, a witness mark showing the path of the cutter will result. This will not necessarily impair the accuracy although it does spoil the finish.

10 *THE CARE OF MILLING CUTTERS*

Cutters are very expensive to buy so it is worthwhile taking care of them. One of the first problems likely to be encountered in the home workshop is rust. This is usually caused through warm air striking cold surfaces which creates condensation. As milling cutters are made of steel they tend to be somewhat colder than the surrounding air and so attract this condensation which will turn to rust very quickly. Rust is, in fact, oxidization of the steel and, if the cutting edges oxidize, a minute powdering takes place which removes the sharp edges. Rust can be prevented in several ways. Prevention of the condensation situation in the workshop itself is the obvious first step if at all possible, although this is not quite so easy as it sounds. My own workshop is exceptionally well insulated and has a small electric heater going day and night. Even so, I have known what amounts to freak humid conditions that have left some items running with water.

Cutters can be stored safely, and with no danger of damage to the cutting edges, by placing them in suitably sized holes drilled in a wooden block. The method also makes them easier to find and is economical on space too.

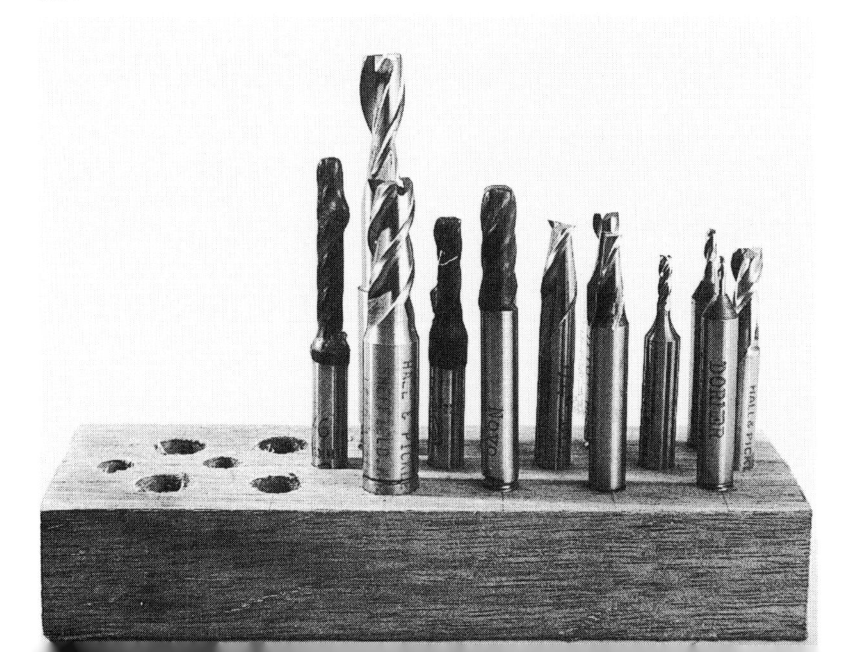

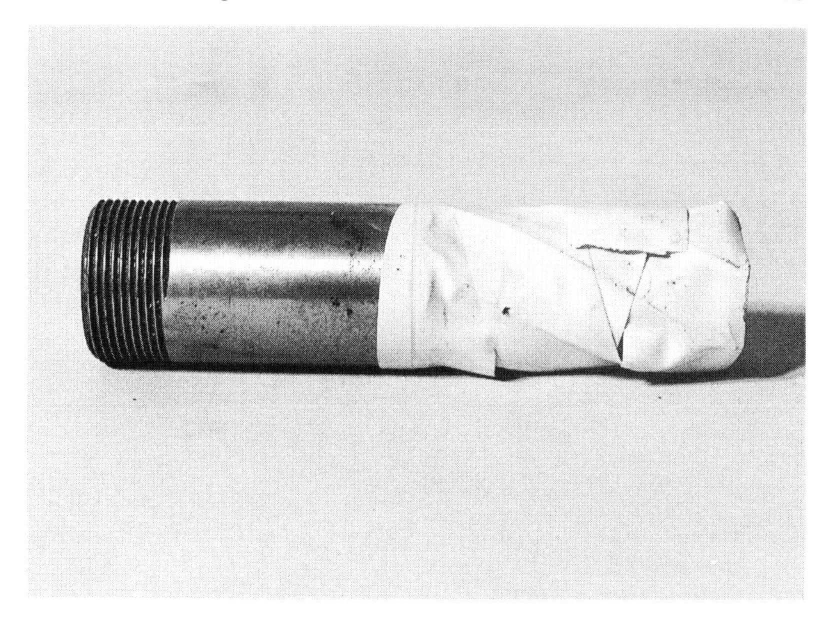

If for any reason it is essential that cutters are stored in a drawer then protect them by wrapping the cutting edges with masking or insulation tape.

Keeping the cutters in a cupboard or in drawers will help as the air inside tends to have less contrast with the outside air. It is, however, as well to 'paint' or spray the cutters with an oil that will separate water from the metal surface. These oils are readily available, WD40 being the trade name of one of the best known. But there are many similar substances available. One such oil which can be obtained in bulk is 'Duck Oil'. Another which will do the trick is know as Ensis, somewhat heavier than Duck Oil but equally effective. It is used in steam engine cylinders for the purpose of preventing condensation. If none of these is available then ordinary grease will help. When cutters are purchased new they usually have a soft 'rubbery' plastic coating which can be removed for use. This coating not only prevents the cutting edges from rusting but also protects them from other damage, so it is worth replacing it on the cutter until it has deteriorated to a point where it is no longer of any use. The plastic used for this purpose can, in fact, be purchased in a spray can. If cutters are to be laid up for some time, or are not used regularly, it is worth investing in a can because of the protection it will give. (A suitable coating called 'Strippable Coating' is made by Arrow Chemicals of Swadlincote, Staffs.)

Cutters should be stored, if possible, in wooden blocks to prevent the cutting edges rubbing against each other. A simple block of wood in which a number of holes have been drilled, and into which the cutters' shanks will fit is all that is required, and this will ensure that the edges remain keen as long as possible. If for

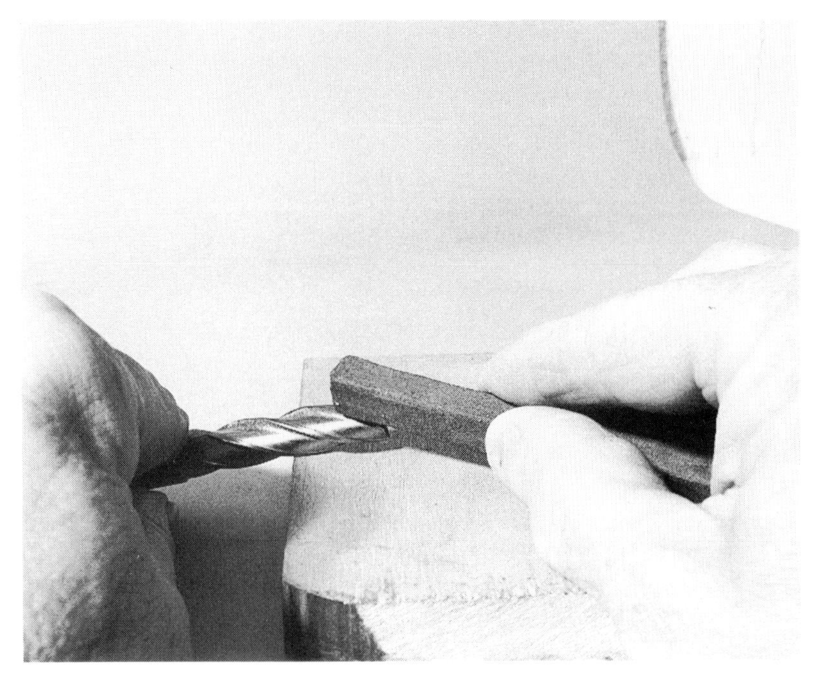

Special equipment is required for cutter sharpening but a rub with a well oiled stone will help to restore them to some degree.

any reason cutters have to be kept loose in drawers or tins, then their edges should be protected in other ways. Wrapping in paper retained in place with an elastic band will help and if newspaper is used it also helps prevent rust providing it is in the first place thoroughly dry. Alternatively, insulation tape or masking tape bound round like a bandage will provide good protection.

Apart from taking care in the first place, keeping cutter edges sharp is a problem. There are specialist firms that will sharpen them, and it may be possible in the case of slot drills to just trim the cutting tips on a grinder. A simple jig could be made for the grinder to give the correct angle. Edges can be retrieved a little by carefully rubbing along them with a small oilstone, and for the sides of cutters this may be the only way. A slight improvement on this can be obtained with a diamond lap. These small laps are not expensive and are sold for touching up carbide tools. They will work very well indeed on high-speed steel from which most of our cutters will be made.

Cutters will always last longer if run at the correct speed and if suitable lubricants are used. Once they have been used on mild steel they do not work well on brass and they are almost a disaster on gunmental which they will tend to skate over. If milling grooves, a worn cutter will tend to push the metal rather than cut it. Neither will a cutter previously used on steel be as good on cast iron, particularly when cutting through the outer shell of castings. I keep new cutters for use on brass, bronze, gunmetal and cast iron and then, when they have had some use, I start using them on steel. At this point they are marked with a drop of paint to remind me not to use them again on brass, etc. unless some attempt is made to improve the edges.

In spite of the rather foreboding paragraphs above, cutters as a rule have a long life even without sharpening. It is possible to purchase special throw-away cutters which are not designed to be sharpened and these have their advantages. They are cheaper than the normal type and as sharpening will be absolutely impossible they are worth consideration. The throw-away types are only available as slot drills or end mills, not as cutters for a horizontal milling machine. There are also tipped cutters to be considered where, when worn out, the carbide tip may be replaced. Such cutters are only available in the larger sizes but, whilst expensive initially, they can be very useful since changing the tips is just a matter of fitting a new one in place with a grub screw provided.

11 *CUTTING LUBRICANTS*

No matter what machine is in operation in a workshop, the use of cutting lubricants is highly recommended. Indeed, even with much hand work their use is desirable to gain the best results. As a rule the first machine that all model engineers use is a lathe, and since the subject of cutting lubricants is as important to the lathe as to the milling machine, some readers may be fully conversant with the use of cutting oils, etc. However, it is a subject that, in my opinion, is well worth repeating because the correct use of cutting lubricants could mean the difference between success or failure in very many machining operations.

If we were to have visited a large machine shop in a factory some fifty years or so ago, and we had never been to such a place before, then probably the first thing that would have struck us was the noise. This would have been followed as a close second by a most distinctive smell caused by a substance known as soluble oil. As the name implies, this is an oil which mixes with water and it was used extensively in machining operations. People working in the industry never left the smell far behind, and even if they washed thoroughly when they went home it still remained; even washing the overalls did little to remove it. Some people loved the smell of it; it was almost like a drug on which they became hooked. Others, particularly those who were not working with it, found it revolting. These days much has been done to change the smells of these oils and different lubricants are also in use. Soluble oil is unpleasant stuff. It can cause skin cancer, if exposure to the liquid is prolonged, apart from the user being ostracized by family and friends. However, in case I am spreading undue alarm, let me point out that medical problems only arise if such oil is worked with over many years, and if the industrial policy of flooding work with it in order to obtain rapid production is adopted.

Let us then look at the question of cutting lubricants bearing in mind that we will be working in a home workshop environment, and try and have the subject sorted out so that we do not run the risks that were present in industry. Perhaps the most important point is that when mixing soluble oil always follow the manufacturer's instructions as the proportion of oil to water is critical to the successful use of the fluid. Different makes of oil will vary regarding the quantities and proportions to be mixed.

So why do we need cutting lubricants anyway? They prevent overheating of both tool and work, they prolong the life of the tool, and they enable a better finish to be obtained on the work. They also allow faster operation, although if we are using the machine in a hobby context, I doubt if the last consideration really has any relevance. The other three have, though, and so we must be prepared to use suitable substances where necessary. However, let us think of them in such a way that we are not going to come out of the workshop to be told that tea will only be served in the garden!

The need for cutting lubricants varies from material to material. When machining cast iron, for example, no lubricant at all is needed and, indeed, if any is used on it there will be a tendency for the material to harden. If work on cast iron is being carried out so rapidly that cooling is required, it would have to be supplied by compressed air, a situation that is hardly likely to apply in the model engineer's workshop. So we can happily machine away steadily at our cast iron and no harm will be done.

Brass is another material that generally can be machined without lubricants, although again it will depend on how rapidly work is being carried out; while on production work, lubricants would certainly be used, in the home workshop the overheating problem is unlikely to arise. The question of tool wear and finish, however, is a different matter and for a good finish we should use a lubricant. Whilst we can use soluble oil, white spirit is far more efficient and as cooling is not too much of a problem it can be applied reasonably sparingly. As a coolant it also has the advantage that it tends to evaporate at high temperatures and therefore is less likely to flow all over the workshop floor. White spirit is therefore the generally accepted fluid to use when machining brass but there are others and at the end of the chapter alternatives will be discussed.

Copper tends to overheat rapidly, which will quickly take the edge off tools, and as we will need to use a considerable quantity of coolant, paraffin is probably as good as any, although white spirit will also work. Another less obvious coolant is 'neat' washing-up liquid which also works well with gunmetal and all the various bronzes.

Aluminium is also a material to which, when machining, it is essential to supply plenty of a suitable coolant. Without it, the soft metal builds up on the edge of the tool and in a short period causes problems. It is almost a self-generating process, as the more the metal builds up the hotter things become, inducing a rubbing instead of a cutting action, thus damaging the tool and spoiling the finish.

The various steels are the materials that require the largest quantity of lubricants and the tougher the steel, the greater the amount required; the machining of any steel without lubricant is

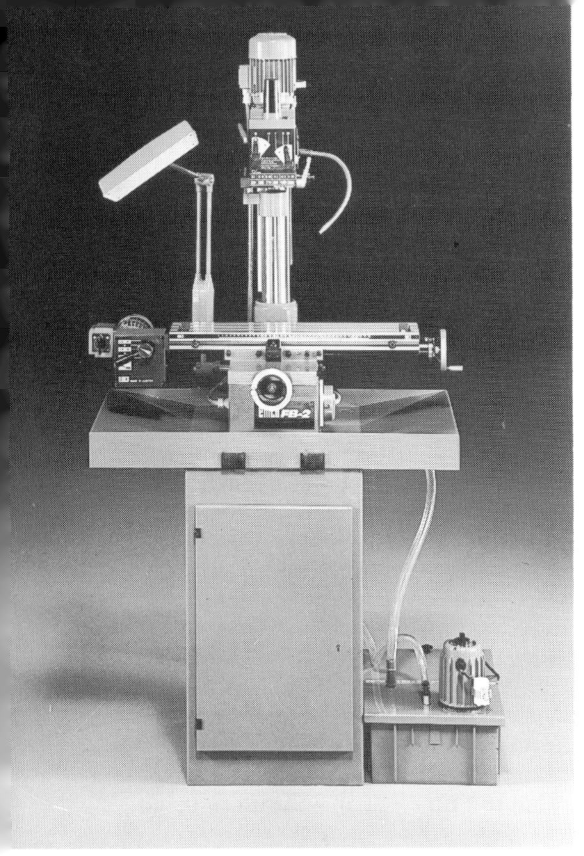

Left *A milling machine by Emco. At the right-hand side can be seen a storage tank for cutting lubricants together with the pump for recirculation.*

Below *The Melsa pump system for cutting lubricants. The storage can at the back holds the liquid, which is pumped via the pump on the left-hand side through the nozzle on the right. The nozzle gives a very fine jet allowing for the lubricant to evaporate. The pump can be hand or foot operated and the nozzle holder has a magnetic base which allows it to be positioned anywhere on the milling machine and directed to any point.*

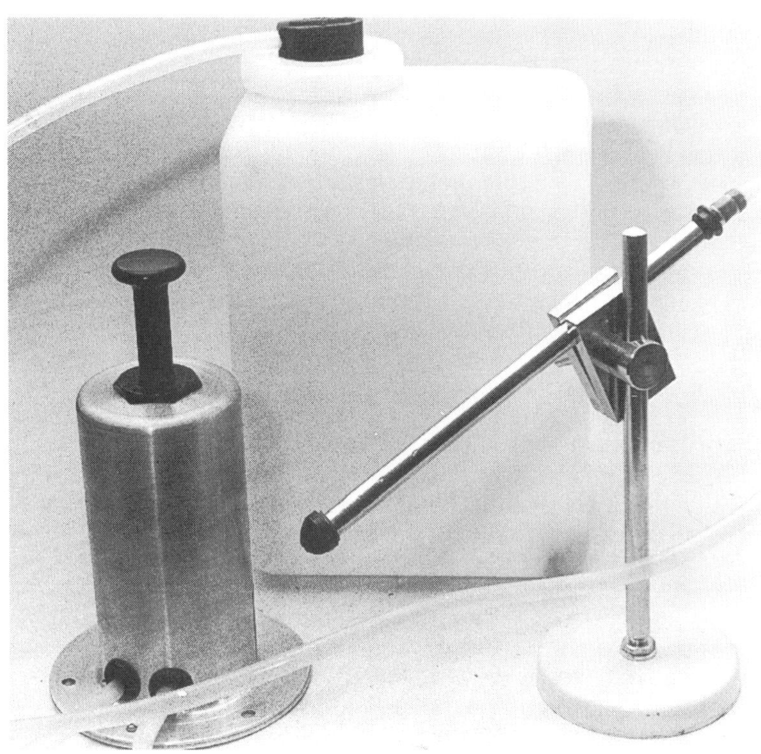

not recommended. Of the traditional lubricants, soluble oil is by far the best and for satisfactory results a steady flow of liquid should be directed on to the work at the point where the cutting is taking place. This can be a messy business in a home workshop and there are now more modern materials available which tend to evaporate and cause less mess.

When machining plastics there is also a considerable heat build-up and frequently the plastic will start to melt and weld itself together. The best lubricant by far is plain water, but a large amount will be needed and it will not do our precious milling machine much good. Apart from soluble oil, another alternative is a strong blast of cold air. Whilst this is possibly the most desirable solution, it is also almost impossible for the model engineer to obtain the power needed or to be able to direct sufficient air to the one spot when it is available. I have tried many experiments with lubricating plastics and have finally settled for white spirit.

These, then, are the traditional types of lubricant which have been tried and tested over many years. The next question is how to apply them. If again we think of industry, cutting fluids are supplied to the work through a pipe connected to a storage tank. This allows a good supply of the liquid to circulate. Having sprayed the work, the lubricant runs on to a drip tray, then through a filter and into a sump where a pump re-circulates it back into the storage tank. The liquid is thus continually circulated round the system and the only loss is from splashing and some evaporation. Such systems are available for use in the home workshop but are, basically, only suitable for soluble oil.

However, there are ways of improvising to provide adequate quantities of fluid to the work. For instance, a simple hand or electric pump coupled to a tank can be made up and indeed such fittings can be purchased. Alternatively, a tin can with a hole drilled in the bottom and a small tap fitted with a rubber or plastic tube running from it to the machine will allow a steady quantity of fluid to flow onto the work. I have such a system using an old paint tin. Although the tin could be supported on a bracket attached to the machine table, mine is fixed to a shelf well above the machine. This is first because I like to keep the machine as clear as possible and a tin on brackets would cramp me for space somewhat, and second that the extra height gives a better flow of lubricant. A small home-made brass tap is fitted to the tin and a plastic tube directs the lubricant to the machine. In order to direct the tube to the point where it is needed, coils of tinned copper wire are simply wrapped round the outside of the tube so that it will maintain its position when pointed in the required direction. The end is usually poked through a hole in a cutter guard when in use and this ensures that the fluid is directed to the exact spot. The guard, only a piece of perspex held in position with a hose clip, also prevents the fluid from splashing everywhere. I have a number of different widths of perspex available to take care of the different lengths of cutters. This system does not recirculate the lubricant. It flows from the

The tin can system as described in the text.

machine tray via another tube into a plastic can where it is then used to replenish the top storage tank.

The paint tin system is ideal where we have a situation requiring a strong flow of cutting fluid, but the aim in the home workshop should, I believe, be to use as little as possible whilst not stinting on the job. With this in mind we can apply the cutting fluids in several other different ways. 'Squeezy' bootles, as used for washing-up liquid, make ideal containers and it is quite easy to squirt the fluid to the right place. Small plastic garden spray cans are also ideal because here we can use the fluid in the form of a mist and in this way the heat will help to evaporate it and there will be little mess to mop up. If we bear in mind the fact that evaporation is also a cooling process, as in a refrigerator, we are now beginning to arrive at a system where we can get the best of both worlds—less mess and greater cooling.

For the operator of the smaller milling machines and the milling attachments, even the methods described above may sometimes supply too much liquid. A device I use where small quantities are required is a pipette often used by chemists, and they can usually be purchased from a chemist's shop. Originally these devices consisted of a glass tube with a rubber bulb on one end. Place the open end of the tube into the liquid, squeeze the bulb, then let go and both tube and bulb fill with fluid. When the bulb is squeezed again the fluid squirts out. These days they are usually all plastic which makes them ideal for our purposes. With such a simple device it is possible to direct small amounts of coolant to exactly the right place.

So far we have covered only the traditional coolants, but these days there are more modern ones that I feel are better for home workshop use. However there are many manufacturers making a wide range, so because of this I intend to deal with types of lubricants rather than makes, as readers living in different districts may have to purchase whatever make their local tool stockist supplies.

Most manufacturers will supply ready-to-use lubricants in handy containers such as spray cans or squeezy bottles. These are designed for specific materials and in my opinion are usually excellent. Some are oil-based but these days a number are solvent-based. This means that they cool the work and the tool but dissolve as they do so, with the result that they leave very little mess. They are, of course, more expensive than the traditional methods. Many of these modern lubricants are either without

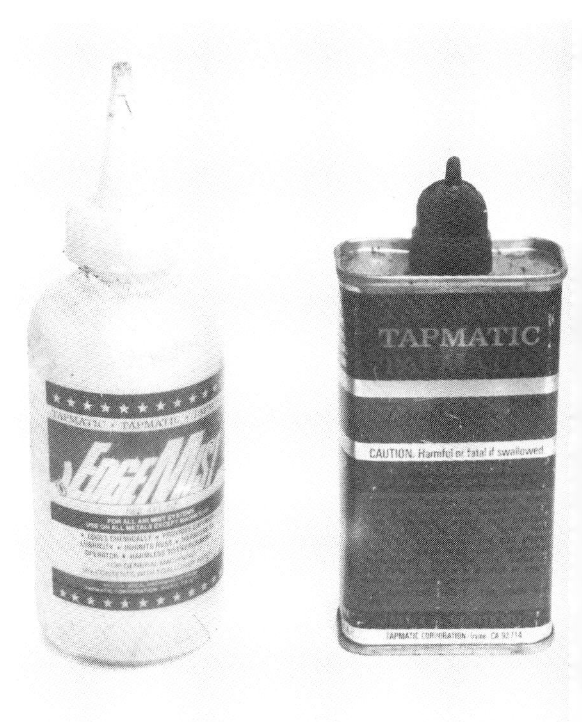

Two cutting lubricant containers bought commercially. Both are absolutely ideal for supplying the correct amount of liquid to the right place. The one on the left contains a biodegradable cutting fluid, whilst that on the right a solvent-based one. The left-hand bottle administers a steady drip; the right-hand one a very fine spray which dissolves on contact with the cutter.

smell or are scented, to make life more pleasant both for the model engineer and the long-suffering family. There are some lubricants which are biodegradable and these are in fact tallow-based. Tallow was probably the original cutting lubricant used many, many years ago by the early engineers and now that it is coming back into use things have gone full circle. One manufacturer even makes one of these in stick form meaning that no liquids are used at all, and the latest offering as I write is a cutting fluid which comes from a spray can as a foam. It can be applied direct to the tool and can actually be seen on the tool, so that when it dissolves one simply applies a little more and in this way there is no need to overdo things. It is well worthwhile obtaining literature from various cutting lubricant specialists regarding their products and choosing that which best suits your requirement.

Finally, returning to the safety angle, no matter what cutting fluid is in use, always wash thoroughly after working with it and, if possible, use a good barrier cream before starting the work session. Where the use of solvents is concerned it may be worth considering using a simple face mask, as some can cause irritation in the throat. Do not let any such lubricants splash around. Soluble oil on a workshop floor is particularly dangerous. A strip of metal fixed along the edge of the machine table will usually retain the lubricant and it should always be wiped off the machine.

Remember only to use the quantity required; don't overdo things; and use the correct lubricant for the job.

12 *THE MILLING VICE*

A considerable amount of work on our milling machine will be carried out in what is called a vice. Like with most such things, there are good and bad when it comes to vices used in milling. There can be no doubt that a good quality vice, in both rigidity and accuracy, will repay the cash spent, but the thing to know is what to look for.

There are very many so-called machine vices on the market but the vast majority of these are not at all suitable for the purpose to which we will be putting them. Most are designed for drilling and are able to take a downward thrust quite well, but they do not have sufficient strength to be able to cope with the sideways thrust required when used for milling operations.

A good milling vice will have a fixed jaw with plenty of metal round it to give it strength. The moving jaw will also be quite substantial and will slide along the bed retained either by dovetails at the side or with a mortice-type system underneath. Either way, the moving jaw should be adjustable and when properly set up it should be possible to tighten the vice without it lifting.

If we take a look at the cheaper machine vices and turn one over, it will be seen that the sliding jaw is retained with a plate held in position with one or two screws, the heads of which may either be raised or countersunk. The plate is usually fairly narrow and fits in a well in the base of the vice. The length of the plate will, to some extent, be the deciding factor on how much the moving jaw will lift when tightened. The longer the plate, the less the lift, if we assume accuracy of fitting in the first place. The adjustment of the screws will of course, also have some bearing on the matter. When material is clamped in the jaws of such a poor vice, the moving jaw, coming under pressure, will try to find a means to escape from that pressure. Since upwards is the only way, it will lift as far as the plate underneath will allow. Because the plates are invariably short, there is bound to be some tilting of the jaw. Only if the plate extends in front of it and is well adjusted can this be prevented.

If we were to look underneath a good quality milling vice, we would find the moving jaw retained over its whole extent by a plate

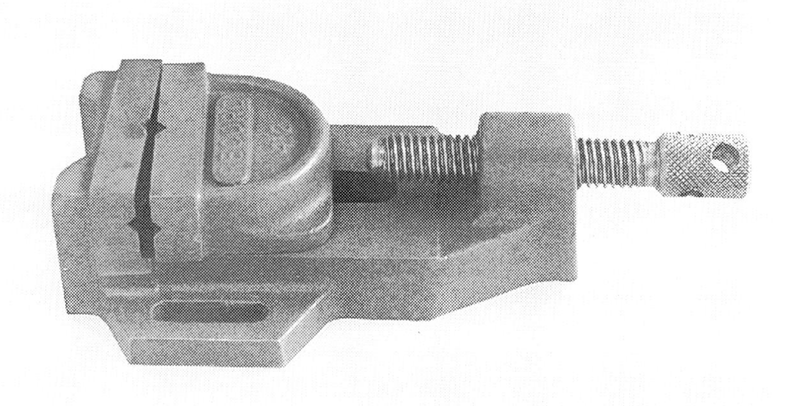

A small vice intended for drilling purposes only for which it is ideal. This particular type is definitely not suited to milling, as, not only does the sliding jaw lift slightly when the vice is tightened, but also it is designed to swivel to accept angular work. This is quite satisfactory when drilling but would never support such work under the pressures involved with a milling machine.

A milling vice on a swivelling base. This is a very substantial example with a good bearing surface for the moving jaw and a hefty lead screw.

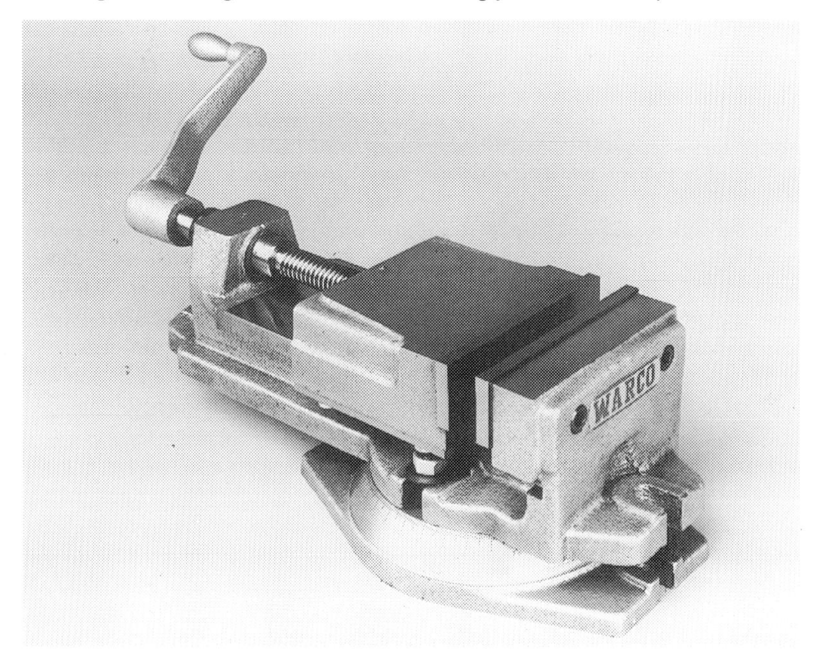

or a dovetail. Because this is parallel with the front of the jaw whilst also being of sufficient length to extend some way down the slide or base, assuming good adjustment, there is no way in which the moving jaw can escape the pressure involved and therefore it cannot lift when it is tightened up.

Another thing to look for in the milling vice is a substantial lead screw, preferably one with a square or acme thread. This screw will be applying tremendous pressure and must have enough strength to cope with that pressure. Most good milling vices have the lead screw covered by a plate to prevent it attracting swarf and dust and creating wear.

The size of vice chosen will depend on the size of one's machine, and the depth of one's pocket. The larger the better must be the answer, as the larger the vice the larger the work that can be held in it. We should not go for size to the detriment of quality, however, as it is always possible to secure large work by other means. If it is possible to obtain two vices of suitably good quality and in different sizes, then life will be easier, but most model engineers, I am sure, probably have to settle for only one.

Some milling vices are made with a swivelling base, thus allowing work to be carried out at an angle, and such vices can even be used for primitive dividing. The base must be a good solid casting since it is no use having a solid vice on a flimsy base. Any swivelling base must cause some loss of rigidity no matter how slight, but the more that can be done to obviate this the better. There is no reason why the vice when in operation should not be removed from the base and clamped straight to the table, using the base only as and when it is needed.

Tilting vices can also be purchased. Any tilting vice must, by the very nature of its construction, lack that essential factor of rigidity. Nevertheless, such a vice may, for some special reason, be required and again a good locking and supporting system is the thing to look for when purchasing.

So far we have established that a good quality vice is essential, but what of the person who for one reason or another cannot come by such a thing? There may be several reasons for this. Cash is an obvious one, but there is also the person who is working with a small machine or a milling adapter on a small lathe. There are not many, if any good milling vices small enough for such machines. We therefore have two alternatives. The first and the one which I favour most is to make our own, using mild steel or from castings which are available. It is not such a terribly daunting task as it sounds and the finished result is well worthwhile. I have made several such vices, either from commercial castings or from castings made to my own patterns. None has taken long to make and all have proved highly satisfactory; the cost has in each case been less than a quarter of the cost of the purchased article.

The second alternative is to modify one of the smaller machine vices that are available. Such modifications are not difficult and, whilst it is not possible to make a silk purse from a sow's ear, it is possible to turn the vice into a fairly accurate and respectable tool. The first thing to do is to replace or modify the plate supporting the moving jaw. It is doubtful if this can be taken from the slot in which it runs, but it can be lengthened and this will make a world of difference. Fit the new one with locking washers to prevent it shaking free. It might also be an idea while the plate is off, to run a cutter along the slot to remove any rough sections that might be present.

Below *A vice designed for setting work at an angle. Although this is quite a cheap one to buy it is quite hefty and its accuracy can be improved very quickly with only a little work having to be carried out on it.*

Bottom *A home-made milling vice from castings by Hemmingway. The sliding jaw runs in dovetails and is adjustable with the screws along the side. The lead screw is covered by a plate to prevent swarf from entering.*

Top *The base of a home-made vice under construction. The long dovetail means plenty of accurate bearing surface for the moving jaw.*

Above *Trueing the fixed jaw on a cheap commercial vice. This operation alone will make quite a big difference to the accuracy of the tool.*

Having at least stopped the moving jaw from lifting too much, remove the plates that are screwed to the jaws, if they have in fact been fitted in the first place. These are frequently quite hard, which is as it should be. Grind off any burrs that might be on them, paying special attention to any round the screw holes. Some of these vices are manufactured very cheaply and no attempt is made to deburr these plates. Having done this, bolt the vice to the milling table and check the squareness of the fixed jaw. Possibly it is not at all square and a milling cutter should be taken across it to get it right. It does not need much as a rule, and we should not take too much off if it can be avoided, as we do not want to weaken the casting. The moving jaw will probably line up when closed, but it may still not be square vertically and if this is so, it must be trued up. To do this it may be necessary first to take the jaw off the vice and to mill a recess at the bottom so that when trueing up, the cutter does not have to touch the slide of the vice. This slight recess will in no way impair the efficiency of the vice.

A good idea is to make another set of plates for the jaws so that you have one hard and one soft. This is a simple cutting and drilling job and when completed they can be placed in the vice, which is then tightened up and a cut taken across the top to ensure they are absolutely horizontal and both exactly the same.

Sometimes it may be convenient to support long work in two vices. These must be identical in size to ensure accuracy. It is here that the cheap vice will come into its own. Two identical vices suitably machined for accuracy will support long work well enough for our purposes and it is a low-priced answer to the problem.

13 *ACCESSORIES*

Having acquired our milling machine and learned the uses of various types of cutters, as well as how these cutters should be used, we should think of what else is required to help us carry out good milling operations. The list of accessories that may be used with the machine is almost never-ending, but these can be built up steadily over the years with much of the equipment being made by using the machine itself.

Constantly referred to throughout this book will be clamps and clamping and so one of the first things we should acquire is the necessary equipment. The main items needed, and these are essential, are tee bolts and nuts. The table of the machine will have several tee slots and tee bolts and nuts are devices that fit into these and enable us to clamp the work in position. Both items are illustrated; the difference is that a tee bolt has a captive nut whilst in the case of a tee nut, the bolt screws into the separate nut which is set in the slot.

Tee bolts and studs. The studs can either be secured in the flat pieces by brazing or with an adhesive, or they can be left separate. If so, they must be prevented from turning and bottoming in the tee slot when being tightened.

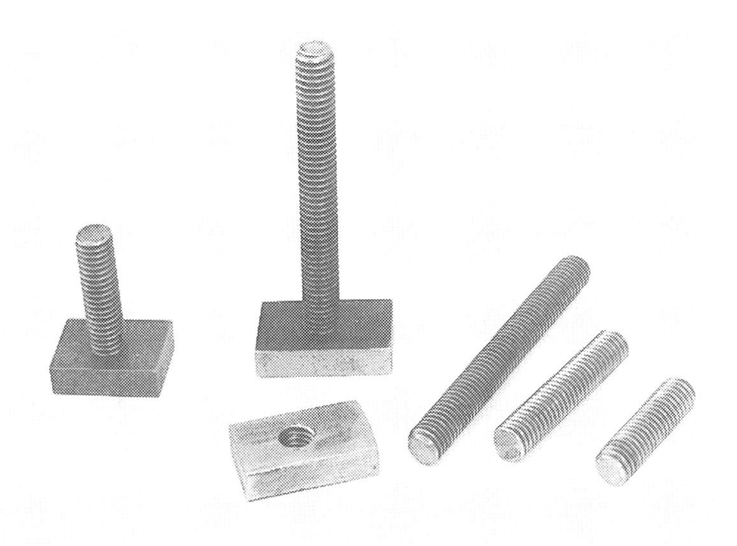

Tee nuts. Designed to accept bolts, tee nuts are at an advantage where there is a need to use a smaller diameter bolt than with a normal tee bolt. The turned boss fits into the vertical part of the tee slot and provides secure housing for the nut. The boss must be of ample length to accept the bolt properly, and the bolt must be long enough to secure the work without bottoming in the tee slot on the milling table casting.

No doubt on many machines it would be quite possible to find that the head of an ordinary bolt will fit into the slot, and this could be used for clamping. But it is most certainly not a practice to be encouraged and in fact may cause severe damage to the table. Tables are cast in almost all cases, and in the vast majority the material used is iron which is very brittle. If an ordinary bolt is used and tightened up hard, there is every chance of the head being pulled through the tee slot and breaking the casting. Whilst almost certainly such damage will be repairable, there is no need for it in the first place. The properly designed tee piece must fit quite accurately into the slot. In order to allow adjustment there will quite obviously have to be some movement but this should be as little as possible. The section of the tee should be as long as is practical so that the strain when the bolt is tightened up is spread over as large an area as possible. The use of tee bolts is to be encouraged rather than tee nuts; there is a distinct danger with the latter that the bolt will 'bottom out' on the table, and whilst ostensibly the work will appear to have been tightened up properly, in fact the bolt will simply be tightening on the table and not holding the work, the result being movement once cutting is started. An alternative is to use tee nuts with studding lengths.

The studding is then screwed into the tee nut and an ordinary nut used for tightening. This method has the advantage that one does not have to keep a large stock of tee bolts of various lengths available but just a number of tee nuts and various lengths of studding.

Below *A commercially made set of clamping fixtures. There is everything here that one is likely to need for clamping work, possibly much more than would ever be used, but worth having as a stand-by.*

Bottom *Home-made tee bolts, etc, on a stand made from chipboard and dowelling, enabling items to be found easily.*

It is possible to purchase sets of tee nuts and bolts together with various clamping devices. Whilst there are obvious advantages in so doing, they are rather expensive and it will be found that many of the items may well never be used. Personally I much prefer to make these things as I go along and to keep them for further use if and when required.

Along with tee nuts and bolts we will need clamping plates. There is nothing complicated about these; they are just pieces of steel plate with holes, or, better still, slots in them. The tee bolts pass through the holes and allow the clamping plate to be clamped over the work and so hold it in position. The clamping plates must be of adequate thickness or they may bend when tightened up. This will not necessarily be noticed but will cause a weakness which will show up when cutting starts. The clamping plate must be higher by a little at the end away from the work to allow the pressure to be put on the work itself. Sometimes this is done by using packing pieces, but some clamping plates have a form of screw adjustment to alter the height.

Clamping plates are again easily made up as required and may then be kept for future use. If the type with an adjusting screw is used, whether it be home made or purchased, then some form of packing, preferably brass, should be placed under the screw when the clamp is tightened up. Failure to do so may result in at the least marking of the table, or in exceptional cases, severe damage.

Commercially produced packing blocks. They can either be used for resting the upper edge of clamps or for lifting the work from the table. They are particularly useful where one end of a component needs to be lifted as the shallow steps provide good graduation.

Top *On the right of the picture can be seen a clamp with a height adjusting screw. These are very convenient and save a great deal of difficulty in trying to find the correctly sized packing. Note that the milling machine table is protected from the bolt by a piece of brass sheet.*

Above *A simply made screw jack and its component parts. These jacks may be used instead of packing where space permits and they allow very fine adjustments to be made.*

Various odd-shaped plates can be made at times for clamping purposes and these should always be kept for use either as they are, or for adapting to other shapes at a future date. Any odd scrap of metal will do and a good scrap box will provide most of what is needed. Packing pieces will also be required for lifting the ends of the clamp, and these too should be retained. Once again any odd chunk of metal is worth keeping for the purpose, although it is possible to purchase stepped packing blocks if one so wishes. Personally I prefer to keep a wide variety of scraps of metal so that I can make or adapt packing and clamps as I need them. In model

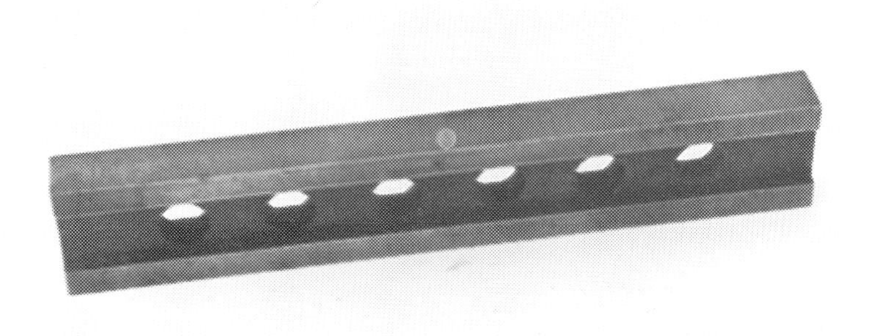

A commercially made hardened and ground parallel. A piece of flat steel bar would do the job equally well, so long as all its dimensions are exactly the same along its length.

engineering some very odd-shaped castings are likely to be used and odd scraps of metal can be adapted for these when often packing blocks just would not work. Washers can also be used as a source of packing and these can be held together with adhesive to make stepped blocks if it will assist. Whilst steel is often used for this purpose, aluminium or brass is better. Not only does it not mark the table of the machine but it also provides a better grip as the clamp tends to bite into it when tightened up.

Sometimes screw jacks are used for packing purposes and these have the advantage of easy adjustment. Once more they are an easily made item and well worth the time spent. Screw jacks and other packing pieces can also be used for supporting work in order to level it.

Something else that is essential is a good set of parallels. These are simply strips of steel of various thicknesses which are used for levelling and raising work. Professionally made parallels are ground to size and sometimes hardened as well. These can be purchased but they are very expensive and this is not really necessary. Ordinary mild steel strips will do providing that care is taken to check that such strips are truly parellel. As strip is drawn or rolled when hot, it may not always be exactly to size and so the pieces intended for use as parallels should be checked with a micrometer to ensure that they are true to size all the way along. They should also be checked for straightness. It is possible to purchase ground mild steel bar at a reasonable price.

Whilst most parallels consist of flat bar there is no reason why round ones should not be used in certain circumstances. Round mild steel that has been ground is easily obtainable and should be used in preference to standard rod. Whenever possible, work should always be set up on parallels whilst operations are carrried out.

Top *An angle plate will be used frequently during milling operations for clamping work vertically.*

Above *An adjustable angle plate. This one is home made from castings.*

So far everything I have mentioned has been designed for clamping work flush with or parallel to the table. However, we must sometimes set work either at 90 degrees or some other angle. For this we use angle plates. The standard type of angle plate will allow work to be clamped at 90 degrees to the table with a good degree of accuracy and the milling kit should include at least one. If possible two identical ones should be obtained since this

A corner clamp designed to be used for square work when clamping on the top of the work is not possible.

will enable very long work to be secured to the table although it is possible to purchase long examples. Whilst the long plate is certainly well worth having for those with a limited budget, two identical angle plates will be better as they will also enable work to be held that is of an odd shape.

For setting work at an angle, an adjustable angle plate may be used in place of an angle vice. These have a swivel action allowing them to be set over to the required angle and work is then clamped to them so that it then takes up that angle. Such adjustable plates come in a variety of designs, and castings are also available for home construction. Castings are also available, of course, for the ordinary 90 degree angle plate.

A separate chapter deals with the milling vice, but there are certain clamps and vices that may be used to secure work that are not true milling vices. As detailed in the relevant chapter, flimsy milling vices should be avoided, but for setting work to an angle there are some which can be used even though their form of construction usually makes them less rigid. The use of one, however, does mean that work can often be set up more speedily than it can with the adjustable angle plate, and if cuts are very light there are some advantages in the use of such a vice.

All these odds and ends may seem a formidable array but they can easily be acquired or made as work progresses. It is never possible to have too many such bits and pieces. While no doubt the object of the vast majority of readers will be to get on with their modelling, the making of tools and equipment is very satisfying and need not take so very long. It also has the advantage that the equipment made is suited to the machine whereas sometimes, when items are purchased, they do not adapt so well.

14 *USING THE MILLING VICE*

The chapters on clamping accessories and vices to some degree cover the clamping of work as well, but a few additional words on the subject is inevitable as so many of the skills required for milling overlap. I hope this chapter will clarify things and make it all seem a bit easier, at least as far as the use of milling vices is concerned.

Work that is square, or has two parallel faces, should be held in the correct type of vice. It should be supported on parallels and in order to ensure that it lies flush with the fixed jaw — which should be the one known to be square — a piece of round bar is placed between the work and the movable vice jaw and the work then tapped down onto the parallels with a plastic or other soft-faced mallet. The vice must be secured to the table with at least two tee bolts, and it must be checked for squareness to the table before starting work. This is unless, of course, work is to be done at an angle to the vertical, in which case a protractor should be used for setting the correct angle.

Round bars, or castings with round surfaces, should always be supported in a vee block as well as the vice jaw. The vee blocks used for this sort of work do not need to be precision tools. Any piece of scrap metal can be milled with a vee for the purpose. The vee need not always be deep; it is simply a case of getting the block to press on two surfaces instead of one and so give the work that little bit of extra support. The vee block made for clamping can be kept for use over and over again. Such blocks do not have to be made of steel, or iron. Indeed, there is a good case to be made out for making the odd one or two from brass or aluminium. These metals being soft will 'give' a little at the edges of the vee when the vice is tightened and therefore offer extra support. The steel block will give some extra support by digging in to the work, but it is possible that the flattening effect of the brass or alloy will do the job better. The use of vee blocks applies whether the round surface is vertical or horizontal.

As we will always be working against the fixed jaw of the vice whenever practical, in order to obtain the greatest support, and therefore the least vibration, the vee blocks should be placed

To set work accurately in the vice, first put a parallel in the open jaws (use two on larger work). Lay the work on the parallel with a round bar between it and the moving jaw and partially tighten up. Tap the work into position with a plastic or other soft hammer and complete the tightening.

Above *A WRONGLY SET CASTING. The flat datum surface should have been against the fixed jaw and a small vee block used to support the round part of the casting.*

Below and bottom *Two views of an awkward component held in a milling vice. The splayed legs made it impossible to grip completely, but there was sufficient material to obtain a hold on the main body. Note how the component was brought clear of the top of the vice jaws for machining by the use of parallels.*

against the moving jaw. With the vice partially tightened up, our old friend the plastic mallet should be used to make sure the work is either flat against the parallels or, in the case of a casting that has no datum to apply to such parallels, is tapped into the required position for machining.

When tightening a milling vice, the correct handle or tommy bar should always be used. The work will need to be held tightly but there is no need to over-tighten. The practice of hitting the handle with a hammer or mallet to tighten it more than hand pressure can achieve is not to be recommended. Firstly, such practice stands a good chance of upsetting the carefully arranged setting of the work. Also there is every possibility of breaking the fixed jaw of the vice. This may sound somewhat far-fetched, but I have seen it done frequently and having taught at technical and secondary schools, where pupils are inclined to get up to such tricks when supervision has lapsed for a second, I can assure readers that at every one of these I have seen vices broken by such treatment.

When the vice is bolted to the milling table, we must make sure it is square and parallel. The table tee slots and base of the vice must be cleaned before the vice is laid in position. Suitably sized and accurate tee bolts should be used for securing the vice, and again there should be no overtightening. Always place a washer under the nuts before tightening. A good pull on an ordinary spanner is enough. Ideally a ring spanner should be used although an open-ended will do. If using an open-ended spanner, watch for the danger of the spanner slipping. Always use a correctly sized spanner and avoid using adjustable spanners, monkey wrenches, or mole wrenches.

Before the final tightening, the vice will need to be set square. A parallel should be clamped in the jaws and the vice squared with a clock gauge held in a bar in the machine mandrel, or on the column if this is flat and will accept a magnetic block and hold it secure. Mill drills have a round column and using a clock gauge from these may be difficult unless your magnetic block has a vee face. It is as well before using the clock gauge to use some means of lining the vice up as close as possible to the final desired position. This can be done with a set square. Using the parallel in the jaw and a square, place a piece of metal in a tee slot and make sure it is flush with the edges of the slot. One edge of the square can rest on this and the other on the parallel and this will give a reasonable degree of accuracy to start with. It may well be that the metal in the tee slot will lie at an angle away from the vice but this will not matter, so long as it is touching the tee slot along its length, as it will still be at 90 degrees to the vice. We are only looking for a guide before making the final adjustment.

If the vice is laid across the table, a piece of metal in the tee slot nearest the fixed jaw, and a parallel between this and the one in the jaw, will again provide a reasonable guide as to how close the vice is to being at 90 degrees to the table. No doubt other methods will be thought of by the individual which will work equally well. Final

Above *A small vice is being set square to the table by using parallels against the vice column. This cannot be done with a machine with a round column. The vice must be finally checked with a clock gauge for absolute accuracy.*

Below *A rough setting check for the vice with a round column machine. A piece of metal is supported in the tee slots and a square taken from this to a parallel in the vice jaws.*

Above *The final check on the vice setting must be made with the clock gauge. With a round column machine this can be supported in the mandrel; on a flat column the column itself can be used.*

Below *To set work square to the vertical, a square can be placed beside it while the vice is tightened.*

Sometimes there is insufficient room to place a square beside the work for checking. In this case, place a parallel across the jaws and a small square on that in line with the work.

lining up must always be carried out with a clock gauge to ensure accuracy.

Some milling operators adopt the idea of placing a sheet of paper between the base of the vice and the milling table. This is intended to help keep the vice in position during the tightening up operations and may be worth considering. An alternative that I use is to make collars that fit over the stud on the tee bolt and are a close fit in the slots of the milling vice. This also helps with setting the vice square (see the diagram).

Work which is to be secured at an angle to the vertical can be held in the vice providing there is enough material on which to obtain a suitable grip. The angle can be obtained with the use of a protractor, or a dodge I use is to mill some pieces of flat bar about $\frac{3}{16}$ to $\frac{1}{4}$ inch, or 5 to 6 mm, thick at set angles. One of these can be laid on the vice between the jaws and the work rested on it. It will then be at the correct angle. If the more usual angles are made on these guides, such as 30-45-60 degrees, they are always then readily available for use. More unusual angles can be made up if

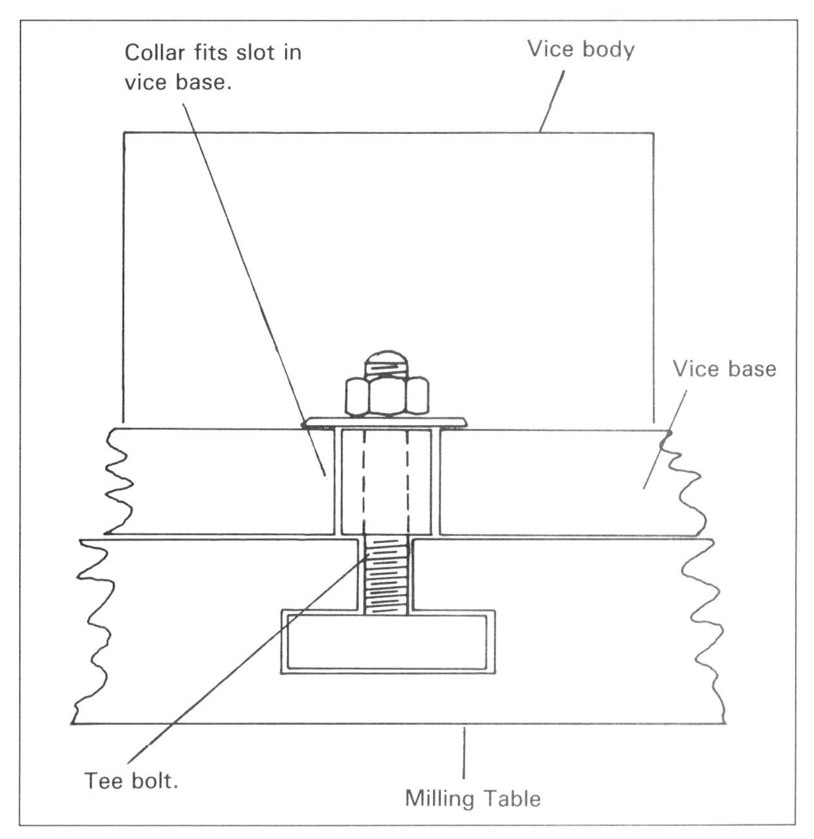

A small collar turned to fit the slots in the milling vice base casting allowing the tee bolt to pass through. This enables the vice to be square with the table. The collar must be made so that the nut will clamp down firmly on the vice casting. If it is allowed to protrude above it, it would obviously prevent the nut tightening right down.

and when needed. For future use it is as well to mark the piece with a scriber showing the angle.

It is possible to obtain machine or milling vices which can be set at angles to the vertical. Like all things, some are good and some not so good. If using one, do not rely for the work setting on the graduations on the angular scale. Always check with a protractor or other precision instrument to ensure that your setting is absolutely accurate.

Angles to the horizontal can be obtained using a vice with a swivelling base unless the reader is fortunate enough to have a milling machine on which the table can be set over at an angle. Once again the angle should be checked and the graduations either on the base of the vice or the milling machine not relied on too much.

Whilst the jaws on milling vices rarely have the fierce hardened serations of the workbench vice, there is always the danger of marking sensitive work. The use of soft jaws is thus worth

Above *Work being set at an angle using a protractor.*

Below *Time can be saved on angular work by milling a piece of flat metal to the known angle. This can be placed between the vice jaws and the work laid on it before tightening.*

Bottom *Work held at an angle in a milling vice whilst cutting operations are carried out.*

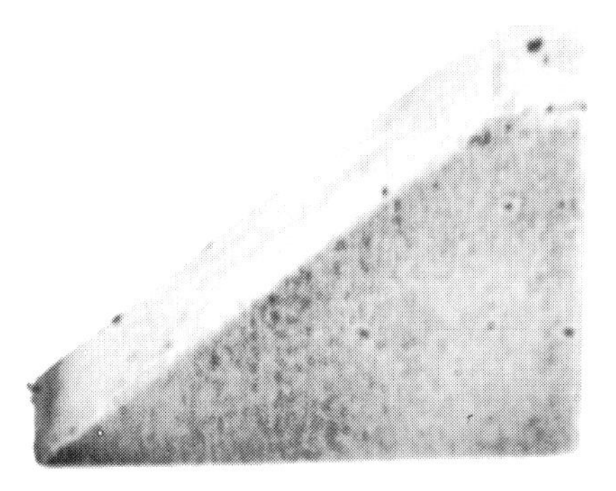

Above *The subsidiary vice in action. Note the grooves milled along the body to allow easy accurate setting in the main vice, and see also how the small vice makes for a clearer view of the component being machined. It would normally be very difficult to see hidden within the large jaws.*

Below *A small subsidiary vice used to hold small work in a large milling vice.*

Bottom *This component, too large for the vice, is supported on each side with blocks and held together with a clamp.*

considering. Normal fibre or plastic soft jaws will not usually provide a suitable grip for the forces involved or be sufficiently accurate. A good idea is to make closely fitting ones from alloy angle. Another alternative is to use carefully folded thin card such as that used for postcards. This will allow the vice jaws to apply pressure through the card whilst preventing severe damage.

Most good milling vices are quite large and holding small work in them can often be something of a problem. I have several tiny home-made vices which I use in conjunction with the main vice. The work is put in the small subsidiary vice and this then tightened in the jaws of the main vice. Not only does it enable smaller work to be gripped more easily but it will stand sufficiently proud of the main vice jaws to allow the small work to be clearly visible during operations.

The milling vice is a quick and easy way of work setting and as such it is invaluable. Do not, however, be tempted to try and use it irrespective of the type of work involved. If work is extra large or of an unusual shape, other methods of securing must be used. As useful as the vice may be, it relies on the work having a suitable surface lying flush with at least one jaw, and without this the security is lost.

15 *CLAMPING*

Although the more regularly shaped work can be held in a milling vice, many jobs will have to be secured with clamps. The chapter on clamping accessories (Chapter 13) covered much of what is needed on the subject. Most work will differ from job to job, so no hard and fast rules can be given on how to clamp work to the machine, but nevertheless I will offer a few suggestions and hopefully the accompanying illustrations will help readers to develop their own ideas.

Work not suitable for holding in the machine vice will have to be clamped. Whilst in many ways the use of parallels under the work is desirable, it is sometimes not practical. For example, in the case of castings the shape may be such that the work will not lie flush to

Commercial packing blocks used to lift a component off the table as an alternative to parallels.

the bed and so the use of parallels is pointless. In these cases it is a good idea to pack a wad of plasticine underneath. This will offer some temporary support to the work but, probably more importantly, will act as a valuable aid to setting up.

Below *A casting secured to the milling table with clamps. The clamps are packed behind the bolt to bring the maximum pressure onto the casting which is supported on parallels.*

Bottom *A more secure form of clamping. Both clamps are supported in a sloping position by hefty packing blocks of mild steel. The casting is resting on hardboard; it has been mounted for boring, and this will allow the boring head to pass right through to the hardboard without going far enough to damage the machine.*

In this case a hole in the casting has been utilized as part of the clamping process. This makes for a more secure arrangement than using clamps only.

When parallels can be used then there should be sufficient support to prevent any vibration or distortion of the work. For example, if we have a comparatively thin piece of work which is also quite long, resting it on a parallel at each end would not be good practice as it would be liable to vibrate in the middle when being machined, so further support must be provided in the centre.

When work is held by clamps, at least two, and if possible more, should be used. I always try and aim for four. I am sometimes satisfied to use three and very rarely I will use just two, but I am never happy in such situations and confine my operations to very light cuts. If the workpiece already has holes in it, then by far the most secure way is to bolt through these if it is practical.

Sometimes, when particularly thin sheet metal is being worked on, there is absolutely no way at all of using either the milling vice or clamps. In these circumstances it is possible to secure the work with double-sided adhesive tape, or a cyanoacrylic adhesive. It is not a practice to be encouraged but, providing cutting is kept very light, it is possible to use the method with some success.

Once the work is satisfactorily clamped to the table or held in the vice then cutting can begin. Do not forget the correct direction of cutter rotation and cut against it. Always try to cut against the most secure section of the work. For example, when the work is held in a vice, cut in the direction of the fixed jaw to provide the most resistance, and cut towards the side which has most clamps if the work is clamped.

A coupling rod for a model locomotive can be a difficult subject to hold in position, This one has been bolted to a piece of scrap angle iron and held in a milling vice. The cutter can be taken right into the angle iron as this will be thrown away after use. It will do for both coupling rods, though, before being discarded.

Another view of the coupling rod, this time being fluted with a woodruff cutter. The steel angle has been turned through 90 degrees and is held to the table with clamps. If the angle iron had been wider, holes could have been drilled and it could have been clamped through these. With the narrow angle, however, this would have made it somewhat unstable on the tee slot which is why clamps were used.

The angle was set in position by lining it up using a block of metal in the tee slot.

Sometimes a piece of bar like this will help support a component at a point where it is not possible to apply a clamp. However, clamps must be used at some point of the setting to prevent the casting from lifting.

Using a square to set an angle plate square on the table. Final checking will be made with a clock gauge.

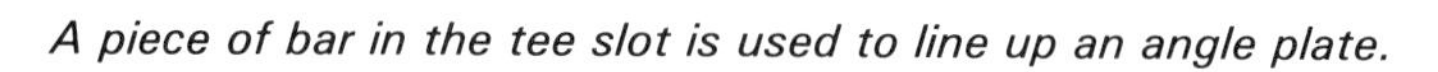

A piece of bar in the tee slot is used to line up an angle plate.

The rather awkwardly shaped component shown on page 90 also proved difficult to set up vertically both ways in order to machine the top and the legs. It was taken care of with an angle plate and an overall clamping piece as shown.

The steam chest seen here had a convenient hole through which it would take two tee bolts so that it could be clamped to the angle plate.

Two angle plates used to support the tender frames for a 5-inch gauge locomotive to mill out the slots for the axle boxes. The frames are held in position with toolmakers clamps and the smaller clamp was inserted because of slight vibration on that side of the work due to the original larger clamp having to be set back due to the webb of the angle plate being in its way.

Another difficult casting, this time a cylinder block set up for facing and boring. The face against the angle plate had already been machined and so was quite flat. As the casting was too big to use clamps on the angle plate, a piece of scrap 4-inch angle was drilled and tapped and bolts with lock nuts inserted. These press the casting home hard against the angle plate giving it ample support.

That part of the clamp directly bearing on the work must always be lower than the other end so that the pressure is applied downwards. Also a washer should always be placed over the clamp on the tee bolt before the nut is placed in position and tightened. If work is to be machined right through, as for example in the case of slot cutting or drilling and boring, it should be placed on something to prevent damage to the table. If it is on parallels, so much the better, so long as you don't drill into them. If not, a piece of scrap copper sheet is a good idea as the change of colour in the swarf tells the operator when the cutter has passed through the work. Another useful medium for this is hardboard. It is strong enough not to distort too much with the clamping and at the same time it is quite obvious when one has got right through the work as sawdust will appear.

Some work will have to be clamped to angle plates. Slots or tapped holes are provided for the purpose and these can be used in conjunction with clamps. However, that end of the clamp away from the work must still be supported so that the pressure on the work is in a downwards direction. An alternative to this is a slotted clamp through which bolts pass on either side of the work. If the angle plate is a good solid one it might be possible to use ordinary bolts in the slots. If, however, there is any suggestion of lack of metal on it, tee bolts must be used to spread the load. Tee bolts will in any event give a far more secure holding.

Thin plate can be held to angle plates with toolmakers clamps in

A flat plate set up for machining using four corner clamps, the clamps are partially tightened, then the two adjacent corners are tightened down hard after checking the position of the component. The other two are then tapped home hard against it with a mallet and finally tightened down.

A casting with sloping edges, and too big for the machine vice, is held in position with knife-edged clamps which dig in sufficiently to make the work secure.

For round work, vee blocks are essential. The normal type of vee block clamp as seen here will almost certainly prove too high and will foul the mandrel of the milling machine. Another means of clamping the work will have to be found.

An alternative to the standard vee block clamp. The overall clamps hold down the vee blocks as well as the work.

A large cylinder block supported on a vee block and clamped down to the table. At least four clamps will be needed before machining can commence. Note the fly cutter to be used will sweep over the whole width of the casting giving a particularly fine finish to the work.

Some castings can be very awkward to machine. Here we see a large cylinder block being prepared for the machining of the port face. Because of its shape, the vee block on which it rests has to be smaller than one would normally wish to use. The height meant using clamps with screw jacks mounted on packing blocks. The whole arrangement was most unsatisfactory. The problem was eventually solved by drilling a hefty round bar at each end so that it would slide over the stud of the tee bolts. This was then put through the cylinder bore and tightened down hard with nuts and washers. This held the work very firmly and when the clamps were put back as shown in the photograph, the work was as rigid as anyone could wish.

The tube of a boiler barrel held on vee blocks and clamped with the use of screw jacks to support the clamps whilst the copper tube is sliced open with a slitting saw. The tape round the tube acts as an easy-to-see mark at which to stop the operation of the saw. It also will act as a guide at a later stage when the tube is cut across its diameter.

perfect safety, and in fact this type of clamp will be quite useful in many situations where it is not possible to bolt through the angle plate, a situation which can often arise for various reasons. Always ensure that the angle plate used is of sufficient height to give support to the work. Any workpiece which protrudes above an angle plate by more than the height of the angle plate itself will suffer very badly from vibration and the finish will subsequently suffer.

When machining is being carried out on clamped work it is as well to check from time to time that the retaining nuts or bolts are not working loose. Should there be any sign of this they must be tightened immediately without disturbing the work. Tightening of clamping bolts should always be carried out in a sequence and there should never be any attempt to tighten right up first one and then the other. Partially tighten the first nut, then go to the nut immediately opposite or as near opposite as possible. Tighten that to about the same pressure. Follow this by going round the other securing nuts, always working on opposite sides as each one is tightened. When all have been tightened to the same degree, repeat the operation until all nuts are as tight as possible. Do not be tempted to hit the spanner with a hammer or slip a piece of tubing over it to obtain extra pressure. The pressure applied with a good spanner will be sufficient.

As work is set up and tightened down it should be continually checked for accuracy. Squares and similar aids can be used for most of this checking but a clock gauge must be used for final checks. Work does tend to move as the clamps are tightened which is the reason for the constant checking, and the methods of clamping described above will minimize the movement.

16 *THE CUTTING OPERATION*

The actual cutting operation, strangely enough, will probably take far less time to describe than all the other various bits and pieces that we need to know in relation to our milling machine. It matters little whether operations are being carried out on a vertical or horizontal machine, or with a milling attachment—the basic principles of the actual milling operation hold good for all.

Having secured the cutter firmly in the machine the most important thing to be settled is the correct speed at which it should be run. This will depend on the diameter of the cutter in use and the material being worked on. There is a formula for fixing the speed and in Appendix 2 readers will find a chart which will save a great deal of working out. As the milling machine will only have a limited range of speeds, we will need to set it at the nearest one below that given in the chart. It cannot be emphasized too much how important the correct cutter rotation speed is, and whilst it is better for the speed to be slower than that required rather than faster, much too slow a speed can be almost as disastrous as one that is too fast.

There are a couple of other variables relating to cutter speed. If the correct cutting lubricant is in use, then as near as possible the correct cutter speed can be used. If for any reason the cutting lubricant is either not used or is used exceedingly sparingly, then the cutter speed should be slowed by some 10 per cent or so. This particularly applies to harder grades of steel. There are also times when no matter how hard we try to get things right, the securing of the work is not as rigid as one would desire. Here again the speed should be slightly slower than that specified but, more important still, cuts must be very light.

The feed is the rate at which the cutter is fed into the work and here again there are correct rates to use. The majority of readers will have machines where the feed is done manually and in this case taking it easy is the only answer. The speed of the feed is in direct relationship to the depth of cut, so the greater the depth, the slower the feed speed. With some practice it is possible to 'feel' both the correct cutter speed and the correct feed rate, and the old milling machine operators always worked on this basis. Should either not be right, the machine will quickly inform you, either by breaking your precious cutter or by making loud protesting noises. Again I have made up a list of such problems for the benefit of readers (Appendix 1).

The direction of the cut is also important. When thinking of this, on a horizontal machine, it is best to look at the action of a cutter and then if need be relate that to the vertical machine. If the teeth of the cutter on a horizontal machine are directed into the metal so that they are cutting in an upward direction, this is called 'upcut milling'. If they have a downward action it is known as 'climb milling' for reasons which will become apparent. For as long as I can recall, it was always considered very bad to use the climb milling technique, upcutting being the only one that was allowed. With the advance of technology, better quality machines and better cutters, the climb milling technique is now not only common but actually recommended in industry. So be it as far as industry is concerned, but whether or not it is sound practice for the model engineer personally I have my doubts. Very few model engineers will have equipment suitable for the technique and more often than not our cutters will not be sharpened to the same high standard either. I think therefore that it is better to stick to upcut milling.

How, the reader may be asking, does this relate to the vertical machine? The answer is simple, really—if we imagine our cutter turned through 90 degrees it becomes horizontal. If we use the end of the cutter, as we so often will, it can then be used to cut work moving in either direction. This applies when milling the top of the work and if the entire diameter of the cutting edges at the end of the cutter are in use. If we are using the cutter to machine just part of the top, so that the whole diameter is not in use, we should use

The teeth of the milling cutter must be made to drive into the work. This is upcut milling. Moving the work in the same direction as the cutter can result in a poor finish, loss of accuracy and possible danger from work being pulled from the table or vice by the pressures created.

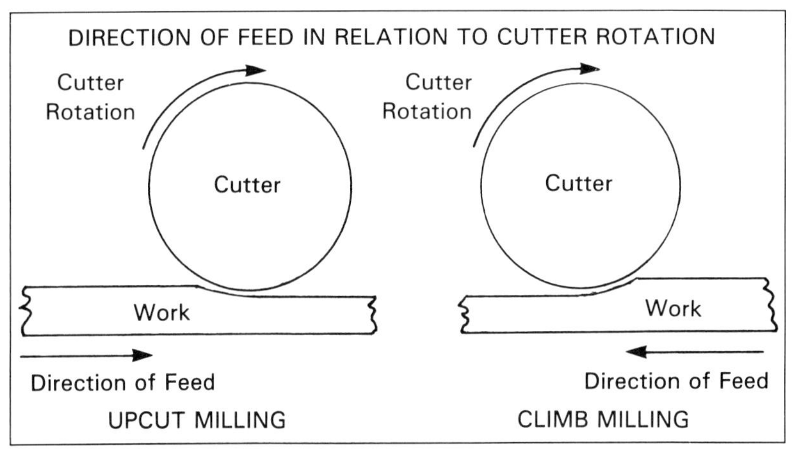

the up cutting process with the work being fed into the rotation of the cutter. If it is fed in the other direction, unless exceptionally light cuts are taken, it will snatch and possibly ruin the work. If we use the side of the cutter the teeth will act like a slab mill on a horizontal machine. With a horizontal machine using a slab cutter, there is an outside chance we might just get away with things, although one dreads to think of the finish so obtained. Using the side of an end mill in this way would be absolutely disastrous.

Below *Using the side of a milling cutter. Upcut milling is essential, so the work will be travelling towards the camera. The tube on the left is for the cutting fluid.*

Bottom *Note the marks on the work caused by the use of an end mill. This work would have been better carried out with a fly cutter.*

When cutting a slot, operate the cutter in one direction only or it will cut oversize.

With a slot drill the effect could be worse and there is every chance of even a large cutter snapping after digging in to the work. The effect is like the caterpillar tracks on a tank. It forces the table along by its action, and we only need the slightest lack of tightness in the securing of the work for it to swing that work at an angle. If the machine being used is of the mill-drill type with a round column and no keyway, the force can cause the head to rotate about the column. The least that will happen is the work will be ruined; the worst could be a rather nasty accident. I can recall at the Model Engineer Exhibition at Wembley one year talking to a well-known and highly respected model engineer who had won many medals for his work. We were speaking about his latest efforts and the coupling rods he had been making. Alas, he told me they were completely written off because he was careless with the last cut and climb-milled, since the cut was not deep. The cutter snatched the work, pulled it loose and that was the end of several hours' careful work.

Another action to be avoided when cutting slots with slot drills is not to be tempted to cut in both directions. If you do there will not be a major accident as I have just described, but invariably the slot will end up oversize. Cutting should be in one direction only in such cases.

Having worked all this out, we can now think about cutting metal which is, after all, what this is all about. It is important to position the work correctly in relation to the cutter ready to start work, and first it will be necessary to establish two or possibly three points of reference. We will need to be able to set the edge of the work to the correct distance from the cutter, possibly in both directions, and to set the height correctly in relation to the surface.

Above *A piece of cigarette paper a couple of thousands of an inch or in thickness is placed on the work. When it is picked up by the rotating cutter, it must be within that measurement of the work.*

Left *When setting work, get down to eye level so that you can see exactly what is going on. Note that the safety glasses have been taken off to give a clearer view.*

Below *Feeler gauges being used to set the tool height from the work. There are frequent occasions when feeler gauges can be used for taking measurements.*

Measuring the first, as I will show, is comparatively easy with even simple home-made equipment, but establishing the height can be somewhat more awkward using mechanical means. What you should not do is to lower the cutter into the work and hope that you have guessed correctly unless you happen to be doing a piece of particularly rough work where the depth does not matter. The technique required for establishing the correct height is anyway really remarkably simple.

Start by popping along to the tobacconists and purchasing a couple of packets of cigarette papers, both of the same brand. Check the thickness of the non-stick part (in fact, the sticky part can be discarded) with a micrometer. Remarkably enough, these papers are produced to a high degree of accuracy and the usual measurement is a one, or maybe, two thousandths of an inch. Having established the thickness, place a small piece of the paper on the work. The chances are that there will be traces of oil on the metal which will hold the paper flat. If not, just wet it so that it will stick to and lie flush on the metal. The machine can be started up and the cutter lowered slowly. When the paper is picked up off the metal by the cutter, the cutting edge is at the correct height, and the depth measurements can be taken from that point, by reference to the hand wheel dial.

Lining the cutter up accurately to the edge of the work can also be achieved by using the piece of cigarette paper in exactly the same way, except that obviously the side of the cutter makes contact with it instead of the end teeth. This method is quite accurate and one that would often be used in industry for finding the correct position. The method can also be used where a measurement away from the edge is used. If we have say, a $\frac{1}{2}$ in or 12 mm diameter cutter and move the work so as to catch the paper, the centre of that cutter is then exactly $\frac{1}{4}$ in or 6 mm from the edge of the work. Using the graduations on the machine it is possible to position the work beneath a certain point of the cutter with the desired degree of accuracy.

Sometimes a 'wobbler' (sometimes called a 'wiggler') is used instead of the paper when working from the edge of the job. This simple device is placed in the mandrel in place of the cutter and brought into contact with the work. The construction is such that it will rotate eccentrically until correctly lined up. It can then be dealt with by using the half diameter measurement of its ball in the same way as I suggested using half the cutter diameter. The wobbler can also be fitted with a small sharply pointed tool. This allows one to correctly locate a particular spot on the workpiece under the cutter and is particularly useful if, for instance, holes are to be drilled in a set position. The use of this device makes the machine very accurate when it comes to boring and similar operations. Wobblers or wigglers (the correct name of which is a centre-finder) can easily be constructed at home.

That explains how to locate the work in relation to the cutter but there is one more important matter to think about. This is the

Above *A sticky pin — a simple dressmaker's pin in a piece of plasticine pressed on to a drill bit. Drawn along the edge of the work any deviation will show up and an accurate setting can be obtained. A piece of white card behind the pin will help you to see it better.*

Below *A wiggler, wobbler or, more properly, edge finder shown here with two components. It is a comparatively simple device, the rods with ball ends fitting into a spring loaded seat. The rod when revolving will at first float off centre, but when it is brought into contact with the work it will indicate when the mandrel is central over the edge of the work. Half the diameter of the rod end should be taken as the figure required to calculate the exact distance from the edge. A cutter should then be inserted and by working out the difference between the size of the rod end and the cutter diameter, the exact measurement required will be found.*

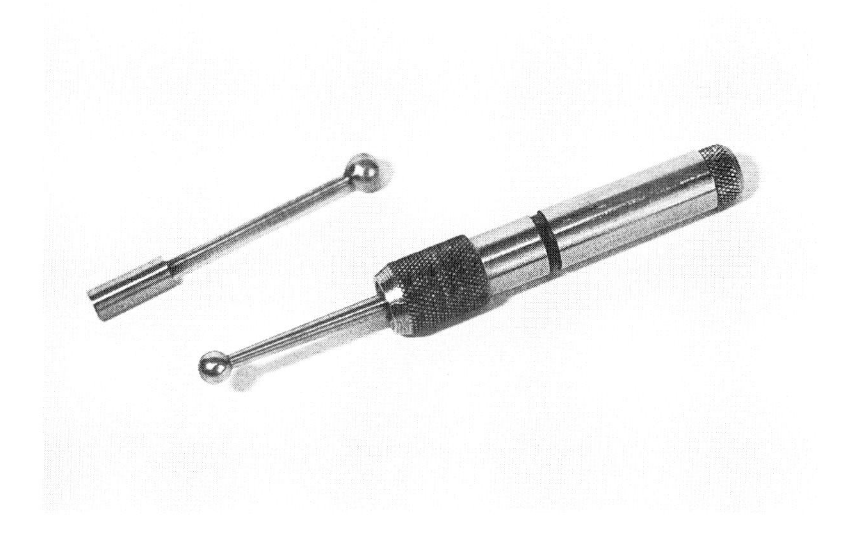

Above *The edge finder in use.*

Below *A simple home-made centre/edge finder. The two ends are a loose fit in the hollow barrel of the tool with a considerable amount of play. They are connected together with a spring. The barrel is fitted into the machine mandrel, and assuming it is being used as a centre finder, the point is brought to the position at which it is wished to start operations. The machine is then set in rotation and if the centre is in the right spot it will run true, if not it will run eccentrically. The bar shaped end is used in the same way as the edge finder. Both these tools should be used in conjunction with a clock gauge to obtain extremely accurate measurements.*

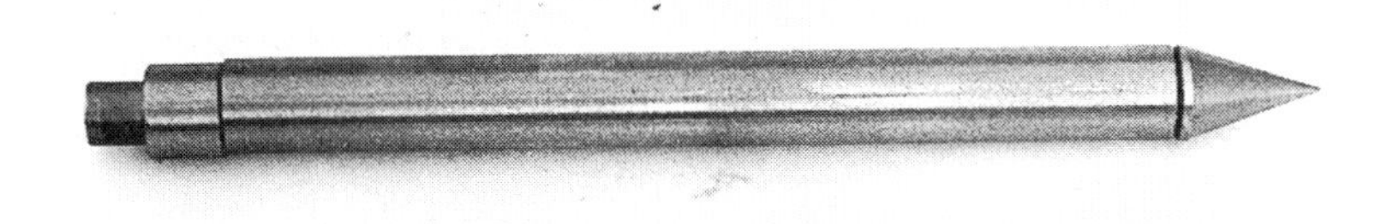

backlash of the lead screw that drives the table and indeed the spindle as well. All milling machines will have some backlash – it is inevitable. Some will have more than others, and some will have an arrangement which allows some adjustment of it to be made. Backlash is the amount of loose movement in the handle and lead screw before driving the table. If we own a milling machine then its degree of backlash should be known to us as it is an important part of the cutting operation. It should therefore be checked when the machine is first acquired and re-checked at intervals thereafter and a note kept of it. Checking it is easy enough. Wind the handle in the opposite direction to the one in which the table is going to move for the purpose of the test. Set a clock gauge, or similar test gauge, to touch the end of the table, in the direction of movement. Set the clock to zero. Take a note of the reading on the handle dial and then carefully rotate it until the clock gauge needle begins to move. Take a second reading of the handle dial and the difference between this and the first reading is the amount of backlash. All three movements should be dealt with in this way and when using the machine, this backlash movement must be taken into consideration. Whatever happens, the handles should be rotated in the opposite direction first to take this up for the machine to be used with the greatest accuracy.

The dial readings should always be used for measurements and there is no need to mark out work for most operations on the milling machine. The dials will be much more accurate than any measurements it is possible to make by eye or hand, providing of course that, as I have already said, the backlash is first allowed for. I find that having a notepad by the machine is an aid to working in this way as details of the readings required can then be noted down. If steps are being milled, or similar operations are being carried out, then take each reading from the same edge which will act as a datum. Do not be tempted to take readings from one point to the next, unless the size or shape of the work makes it impossible to do otherwise.

Some machine tables are fitted with stops and these are most useful as if these are set there is no need to be constantly referring to the dials. If the machine is not so equipped it should not be too difficult to fit them. Some milling machines also have measurements along the length of the table. Whilst the use of these will not give a high degree of accuracy, they can be useful for various roughing out operations and a narrow steel rule could be screwed in position on the table if desired.

That just about covers cutting operations and I must again stress that correct speeds and feeds, as well as correct lubrication, are very important. It is all too easy to think that by taking extra heavy cuts we are speeding up operations. This is not so on most of the milling machines found in the model engineer's workshop. If a very deep or large cut is taken, the speed of the feed of the cutter will have to be slowed down which makes heavy cutting self-defeating. In the long run it is probably as well to take many lighter

Left and below *Thin metal frames for a gauge 'O' locomotive being milled along the top edge. This is always a difficult problem. Positioning them as far in the vice as possible is one answer. However, the main problem will come from the thrust of the cutter. If, as in the first photograph, the cutter is central to the work, the thrust will be sideways across the metal giving almost a screwing action. In the second photograph the cutter has been moved over, with the result that the thrust is now lengthways along the metal and there is less chance of damage occuring.*

Above right *If stops like these are fitted to the milling machine time can be saved by setting them to the beginning and end of a machining run. Also, if working continually to a dial setting, there is danger that the backlash will be overlooked, but working up to a stop this mistake cannot occur.*

ones which can be carried out much more quickly. The final cuts which give the finish to the work should always be light. The lighter they are, the less vibration occurs and the better the finish. Practice makes perfect and the tips given will help with accuracy. A point not so far stressed, however, is cleanliness. Even a tiny piece of swarf left on the table can often mean the datum point has changed. It is therefore essential that the table is wiped over to avoid this before clamping any work to it and taking measurements which might otherwise be incorrect.

17 *USING THE HORIZONTAL MACHINE*

Using the horizontal milling machine is not very different from using a vertical one. Correct cutting speeds, feed and lubrication are points that have to be observed in the same way. This type of machine is less popular with model engineers for a number of reasons, one being the expense of cutters. All cutters for horizontal machines are expensive and furthermore very difficult to sharpen without specialist equipment. Another reason is the difficulty involved in carrying out some small operations such as milling the parts in steam engine cylinders.

Where possible, when using a horizontal machine, cutters should be used that cover the whole of the area to be machined, rather than taking it in a series of steps. Certainly the cutters should be as wide as possible in any event, so that whatever happens the number of cuts are reduced. Depth of cut remains the same and will depend on the material being used, the type of cutter

An operation typical of the work carried out on the horizontal milling machine.

Different types of cutters for the horizontal milling machine.

and the quality of material being machined as well as the sturdiness of the milling machine itself. A side and face cutter is used for milling edges of material which are vertical. For grooves, keyways, etc., slotting cutters, which are rather like wide slitting saws, should be used. Slitting saws with suitably sized bores are mounted on the arbor and used for cutting. With horizontal cutters, the machining of a large flat area was at one time much faster than was then possible with the vertical miller. The multi-toothed large diameter cutter has now remedied that and large flat areas can be covered with that type of cutter as easily as they are with a slab cutter on the horizontal machine.

It is possible to make up single-point cutters for use on a horizontal machine in the same way as single-point cutters are made for the vertical machine. The difference is, of course, that the holders for these will have to be made to fit over the mandrel and a keyway will have to be cut in them to accept the key on the mandrel. For some work cutters can be used in banks. In the case of parallel keyways, or slots, several cutters may be spaced along the mandrel to allow all operations to be carried out at the same time. The same principle can be applied to home-made single-point cutters, several tools if necessary being inserted in a single collar. This idea will allow one to cut the parallel ports of a slide valve system engine cylinder but with a depth rather less than that which can be obtained with the vertical machine.

All in all, if room and funds allow, the horizontal machine can be useful for the machining of large work. If only one machine is to be obtained, however, the vertical type will prove by far the most useful to the model engineer.

18 *GENERATING CURVED SURFACES*

A rotary table is the tool that is used for generating curved surfaces with a milling machine. The device consists of a base, usually a casting, on top of which is a circular table having a number of tee slots. It may also have a number of circles engraved on it which are there to aid in setting up work. The table is connected to a hand wheel via a worm gear and shaft, the ratio of which determines the number of turns of the handle required to complete one revolution of the table. On some tools it may be possible to release the gear

A standard type of rotary table that can be used either vertically or horizontally.

Top *A small home-made rotary table designed only for horizontal work.*

Above *A small rotary table designed to be used on the vertical slide of a lathe. It is available as a set of parts and is fully geared or it may be operated by hand using the tommy bar.*

and rotate the table by hand, to enable it to be set to the required position to start milling without the necessity for winding the handle many times. The handle should have a graduated sleeve which can be adjusted for setting by releasing a locking screw. There are almost certain to be graduations round the table which will read from zero to 360 degrees. There should be a locking device so that the table can be held in one position and will not rotate until the device is released. Some rotary tables are combined with dividing heads.

Using a rotary table to mill the spokes of a fly wheel for a model stationary engine.

Work can be bolted directly to the table using the tee slots, or may be held in a machine vice, which in turn is bolted to the table. There is no reason why work should not be bolted to either a vee block or an angle plate secured to the table, which, in fact, can be used exactly as one would use the main milling machine table. When the workpiece has been secured firmly, the cutter is brought into contact with it, and the handle rotated thus generating a curve.

Suppose then we are to make a curved edge on a piece of metal using an end mill. The first thing to do is to align the centre of the rotary table directly underneath the mandrel, making sure that it is exactly central, and parallel to the edge of the machine table. When the work is secured to the rotary table, we must make sure that the axis of the curve we are going to mill is exactly on the table centre, which we have already established is under the mandrel centre. The milling machine table can then be traversed along so that the centre of the mandrel lies exactly over the line of the radius of our curve. Cutting can now commence by rotating the rotary table over the length we wish our curved surface to be. The accurate measurement of this may be obtained by reference to the graduations on the table. When operating the rotary table, the slides on the milling machine must be locked hard to prevent any unwanted movement.

A somewhat unusual milling machine, the Sigma-Jones, where the milling table itself is actually a rotary table.

The sequence for use of a rotary table: **Above** *Find the table's exact centre beneath the mandrel;* **Below** *secure the work to the table and check that the axis point of the desired radius is exactly central to the mandrel;* **Above right** *line up the mandrel centre with the middle of the cut to be made;* **Below right** *cut the slot as required.*

As readers can see, the process is virtually the same as ordinary straightforward milling. The type of work which the model engineer will usually carry out on a rotary table is the making of locomotive coupling and connecting rod ends, expansion links, etc. Usually the metal used for these will have a square end and rounding this off may be something of a problem as the cutter will be inclined to catch the corners and force the table round. It is essential therefore that either such corners are first roughly rounded off with a file, or that the initial machining is carried with extreme care to prevent such snatching taking place.

Marking out the work first can be especially useful when using a rotary table, as it gives some idea of what we are trying to achieve. It is fairly simple to imagine a straight line on a workpiece, but a curved line on an object is more difficult. However it is not by any means essential as it is quite possible to work quite accurately using the machine's graduations only.

Unless cutting slots with slot drills, the diameter of the milling cutter in use should be as heavy as possible as the forces in use on a rotary table obviously do not travel in a straight line and there will be some whip with a light small diameter cutter. Really it is all a matter of pure common sense; the smaller the diameter of the cutter, the smaller the cut to be taken, and there will be no problems.

Most rotary tables can be used either vertically or horizontally. Although most often used in the horizontal position, there are times when it may be necessary or simply convenient to mount them in a vertical position.

Rotary tables are available in a variety of sizes and the choice will, to a large extent, depend on the size of milling machine on which it is to be used. Six inches is a nice general size but the larger the better if there is sufficient space on the machine table. Of course, prices will most definitely be considerably higher with the larger tables.

It is quite possible to make one's own rotary table and a number of firms supply the necessary parts and castings, and such tables can be equally as good as the commercially manufactured tool. It is possible to make, and indeed to purchase, the casting for a rotary table that does not have a worm drive operation. Designed by George Thomas, who was something of a genius when it came to designing machine tools, the table is simply pulled round by hand with a tommy bar. It is a cheap and cheerful rotary table and providing care is taken will work very well, and cuts must be very light because the table is running free. Also the use of such a tool does mean extra care being taken over safety as the hands will be in contact with the table whilst the rotating cutter is working on the metal. This type of table is only available in a small diameter but it is a useful idea if a proper geared type is beyond the reach due to expense.

19 *DIVIDING*

Quite frequently it will prove necessary to 'divide' with the milling machine. No matter what type of machine is in use, the principle of division is exactly the same. The work is secured to a special attachment which allows machining to be carried out in divisions. That may sound somewhat complicated so let us think of some examples: putting a square end on a shaft is one that readily comes to mind, as does making a hexagon section to be gripped with a spanner. However, there are many occasions when division is essential. For example, if we have a round bar on which we wish to machine a square end, the bar should be milled with the first flat and then rotated through 90 degrees, and a check made with a square that the flat section just milled is absolutely vertical. The second flat can then be machined, the bar rotated and checked with the square again until we finish up with a perfectly accurate square end to our bar.

We can also work by calculation, the number of divisions required being obtained by dividing the chord of the bar by the diameter (see Appendix 3). The bar can be marked out and we can machine the flats to the marking. However, a number of errors can creep in. It would be fortunate indeed if the diameter worked out to only one or two decimal places, but it would be virtually impossible for the chord to work out to any less than six places. The multiplication could well give us a figure to eight decimal places. It would just not be possible to mark out using normal marking-out tools to that degree of accuracy. But just suppose that everything went our way and the figures did come out to a nice round number. Could we then machine by eye to the required degree of accuracy? I think not.

The best means of dividing is to use a device known as a dividing head. It is also the only system that will give virtually an infinite number of divisions. The device consists of a worm wheel connected to a mandrel. The mandrel is supported in the main body and the opposite end to the worm wheel has a fitting such as we would find on a lathe, thus allowing work to be supported in the same way as it is on a lathe, using either a chuck, a face plate, or

A dividing head by Warren Machine Tools Ltd. Three dividing plates provide for a full range of divisions, and work can be supported either in a chuck or a face plate. A tailstock device is supplied to provide additional support when necessary.

supporting it on a centre with a catch plate and driving dog to allow it to rotate. Usually the other end of the work will be supported on a centre, as it would be on a lathe, a special centre block which matches the height of the dividing head mandrel being part of the standard equipment.

A single start worm is fitted at right angles to the worm wheel and connected via a shaft to a cranked handle which is called the index crank. The arm of the crank will have a slot in it and in that is a peg that can be slid up and down. This peg is a close fit in the holes in a dividing plate, which is a plate usually of steel in which are a number of holes spaced evenly in circles around it. The plate may carry several circles of such holes the number differing in each circle. It may then be a plate with circles containing 25–30 and 35 holes, or have as many as 10 rows of holes. The dividing plate fits over the worm shaft, but does not rotate with it. The ratio of the worm and wheel will vary from make to make, but 40 or 60 to 1 are the most usual. Let us for the purpose of this explanation assume that the gear has a ratio of 40:1. This means that for every complete turn of the index crank, the work, which we will assume is mounted in a chuck will travel $\frac{1}{40}$ of a circle. It is easy to see that using the crank handle alone we can divide the work into 40 parts or any direct division of 40. If only all the work we were ever likely to do that needed dividing were to be divided into these amounts, that would be the end of things. Alas, life is not as easy as that, so if we do not need a number which will divide into 40 exactly, we need to use one of our dividing plates to obtain the number of divisions we require.

A little bit of simple mathematics will be required to arrive at the figure we want, so let us assume that we are going to divide the work into 13 equal parts. We know that 40 complete turns of the crank will give a complete circle, so to get the number of turns we need for a single division we must divide 40 by 13. This gives us the figure $3\frac{1}{13}$, which means that we will need to rotate the crank three complete turns and one thirteenth of a turn to get the required division. This is where the index plate comes in. The peg is set into a plate in such a way that it will give a thirteenth of a complete rotation of the crank. It is unlikely that a plate will be available with 13 holes but we could use, say a 26-hole plate and use every second hole, or a 39-hole one and use every third hole. So to sum up what happens: the crank is rotated in complete turns and parts of a rotation are taken from the dividing plate. The two combined will give the required number of divisions.

It all sounds a little complicated to explain but once the device has been used it becomes comparatively simple. It can be seen what a nice convenient method it is and how with enough plates virtually any division can be obtained. However, it is very expen-

A simplified dividing head by Cowell. It is capable of a full range of divisions and is made to accept a standard Cowell chuck.

sive to purchase a dividing head, and the plates too are expensive items. Of course, some model engineers make their own and this is not all that difficult. A rotary table used vertically can be used to get divisions by referring to the degrees marked both on the table and the handle collar, but this will not cope with many of the odd numbers which might be required.

For lesser mortals simpler methods are called for. One way round the problem is to make a simple dividing head oneself. This will involve making a block of steel carrying a mandrel and bolted to the table of the milling machine. The mandrel must be capable of accepting a face plate or chuck, and there must be some means of locking the mandrel when it has been rotated to the correct position (see the illustration below). To the mandrel we connect either a dividing plate as described above or, cheaper and easier still, a gear wheel. If some form of locking detent is made to fit into the teeth of the gear wheel, then it can be rotated to the same number of divisions it has teeth. Of course, we will probably not want that many divisions so if we are using a 60-tooth gear, say, whilst wanting to divide the work into 10 divisions, we simply take every sixth tooth as our point. So long as the number of teeth is divisible by the number of divisions required, there will be no problems.

A very simple home-made dividing head. It utilizes change wheels from a lathe, and therefore is somewhat limited in scope but even so it will give quite a wide range of divisions. A detent locks into the lathe gear wheel at the required division and the screw on the top locks the spindle in position whilst work is carried out.

Top *Milling the square end on a shaft using the home-made dividing head fitted with a three-jaw chuck from a lathe.*

Above *The Cowell dividing head used here for cutting splines on a shaft, using a gear cutting wheel to obtain the right shape.*

The disadvantage of this method is that we will not be able to obtain quite the number of variations that we would by using a proper dividing head, but for most purposes there will be sufficient positions available. If we use the change wheels from the lathe, or indeed if we purchase such wheels specially, it is possible to collect gear wheels in series of five teeth from, say, 60 down to 20 so you will see that there will then be a wide range of divisions available. Even so, sometimes the right gear wheel will not be to hand and it may be necessary to improvise. A recent job I had to do required me to graduate a shaft to 24 sections. None of the gears would divide to this figure but the answer was fairly simple. I took a 60-tooth wheel and, using every fifth tooth, obtained 12 graduations. Then I carefully marked the work to divide one graduation in half. This I checked several times to ensure absolute accuracy then once the work was positioned by using every fifth tooth again I had my 24 divisions. So you see it is like most engineering problems. Think about it for a while and there will usually be a solution.

Often it will only be for graduating purposes that very high numbers of divisions will be required, so our gear wheel device will usually do the job very well. If the tool can be made to position vertically as well as horizontally, its versatility will be much increased. One job for which dividing will certainly be necessary will be gear cutting, but again our gear wheel combination will usually be sufficient for any gear we are likely to need, unless we are making clocks when some form of division plate is virtually essential.

When working with a dividing head, the work will not be quite as well supported as when laid directly on the table or held in the vice. It is therefore necessary to take much lighter cuts than normal to prevent chatter and vibration. Fortunately, when gear cutting, squaring shaft ends, etc., we are generally not looking to remove much metal rapidly, so there is no reason why the dividing head should not be used with success.

20 *DRILLING, BORING AND TAPPING*

There is no reason why drilling, boring and tapping should not be carried out on a vertical milling machine. Some machines of course are designed so that a simple clutch converts them from a milling machine to a drill machine. With or without this function, drilling operations can still be carried out.

Any work that is being milled on the machine and will subsequently be drilled and tapped, or just plain drilled should always have these actions carried out whilst it is still in position on the table. In this way the accuracy of the machine can be used for

Using a centre drill before drilling in the milling machine.

Above *Tapping a drilled hole whilst the work remains* in situ *on the milling machine.*

Below *A facing and boring head shown here in the open position for facing, and closed for boring. In the latter photograph the graduated adjuster can clearly be seen.*

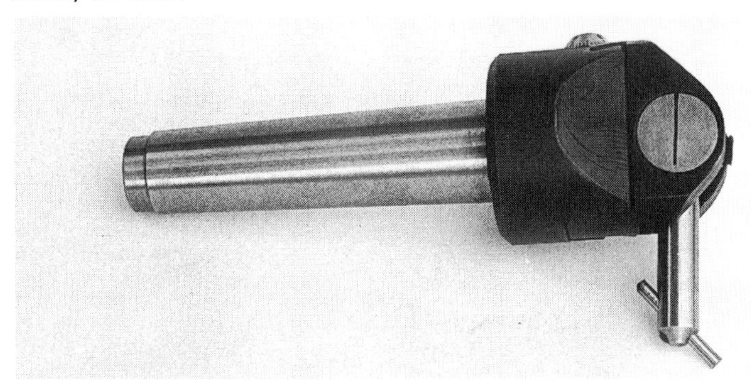

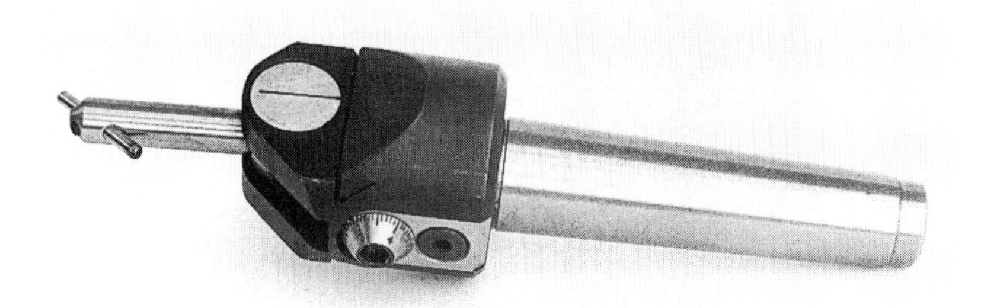

A home-made facing and boring head being used to cut the fire hole in a boiler plate. The tool was left at the extended length as it was also used for other purposes, and as it will not foul the work it will do no harm.

The facing and boring head used to cut an oil groove in a casting. The advantage of these tools is their versatility. At one setting it is possible to bore, face and undercut by just adjusting the tool.

locating the holes. Holes should always be started with a centre drill before using the drill. However, there may be a slight snag here because centre drills are somewhat short in length, whilst large diameter drills are very long. It must therefore be established that both centre drilling and drilling can be carried out without the need to raise the head of the machine in between each operation because that could lead to loss of accuracy. This will only apply to machine with round columns. Most machines which operate with the table lifting up towards the head will have ample movement for both operations.

In the event that both operations cannot be carried out without changing the head position, an extension can be made up for the centre drill. It only requires a bar of mild steel with a hole drilled axially to take the centre drill, and another cross-drilled and tapped to take a grub screw to prevent the centre drill from rotating within the holder. Like all these bits and pieces we make up, it will always stand us in good stead later on.

Tapping of the holes can be done with the tap in an ordinary tap wrench, a centre in the milling machine drilling chuck locating in the end of the tap, acting as a guide to keep the tap straight whilst it is cutting the thread. The same precautions apply to drilling and tapping in the milling machine as would apply for normal drilling and tapping operations at the bench.

Boring holes to a high degree of accuracy is possible by using a boring and facing head. This simple but effective tool is a boring bar such as we would use in the lathe; it is set in a holder which allows it to be adjusted for diameter which is measured by a dial on the tool. It is possible to obtain boring heads that are self adjusting, but these are very expensive and it would be hard to justify the cost involved for a hobby. An ordinary simple boring head can easily be made.

For anyone without the luxury of a boring head, holes can be bored to a fair degree of accuracy by using an ordinary boring bar with an adjustable tool. This does mean that the tool has to be adjusted after each pass through the work by undoing the retaining screw and pulling the tool bit out a little, but doing so with absolute accuracy is difficult.

21 *METALS*

A knowledge of the machining properties of the metals on which we are likely to be working is essential if we are to achieve the best results. Apart from obvious things like different cutting lubricants required and different cutting speeds, observation of how a metal is reacting to the machining will tell us whether or not all is well.

MILD STEEL

The very term mild steel is used to cover what amounts to a whole range of steels. I do not intend to go into the various compositions of the grades, but suffice it to say that the model engineer is likely to come into contact with several. Free cutting mild steel is specially prepared so that it is, as the name implies, free cutting when it is machined. Other mild steels will be in a variety of

The correct formation of swarf is one of the best guides as to whether or not the milling is going well. Here we see four examples of good swarf formation. **Below** *Cast iron,* **top right** *Mild steel,* **middle right** *Brass,* **bottom right** *Bronze. Each is quite distinctive. Any sign of discoloured or powdery swarf is an indication that all is not well. (This is not a guide in the case of swarf produced when using a lathe for turning.)*

degrees of hardness but they will certainly machine differently from the free cutting variety. Whilst the latter is very nice to work with, they are not always the best as far as wearing properties are concerned so we will sometimes need to use others.

The chips created by cutting any type of mild steel should be bright and should curl slightly as well as being thrown clear of the work when any form of face milling is employed, including the use of sides of end mills. When the end teeth of end mills are being used, long rolled pieces of swarf should come away with the free cutting varieties and shorter curled ones with the harder steels. A good supply of coolant is essential for milling mild steel as heat builds up very quickly. If the chips start to come away smaller in size and discoloured, the work is becoming too hot. This will either be because of lack of lubricant or because the cutter is worn. With some of the harder varieties of mild steel, cutter wear is indicated by the metal taking on a glazed appearance.

CAST IRON

This is a material frequently used in model engineering, usually in the form of specially shaped castings such as cylinder blocks, etc. Sometimes cast bars are used to make components. There is always a hard skin on cast metal and where possible the first cut should be deep enough to pass right through this. Whilst high-speed cutters are satisfactory, if carbide tipped tools are available these will give better results. UNDER NO CIRCUMSTANCES USE A CUTTING LUBRICANT. The use of such a lubricant will cause hardening of the iron which will become difficult or even impossible to machine. Worn cutters are indicated by a glazed appearance on the metal being machined and this too will cause the iron to harden. Frequently, cast iron will twist out of shape badly after machining. In fact, all castings should be allowed to spend six months or so in the garden getting well rusted to prevent this happening! Machining rusty iron is not a popular pastime with model engineers, however, so this rarely happens. If time is not at a premium, the machining can be partly carried out and the casting left to distort if it will, and the final machining operations carried out later, which will then bring it back to shape. When machined, the iron comes away in the form of tiny chips and dust. It tends to fly around all over the place and so the wearing of a face mask to prevent it getting in the throat is a wise precaution. The dust of cast iron is very abrasive and care must be taken to clean the slides and other working parts of the machine as thoroughly as possible after machining. All castings are likely to suffer from blow holes. These are holes that appear during the machining operations and usually just on the final cuts. Foundries will invariably exchange castings having blow holes but a less troublesome way would be to fill them with a mixture of epoxy adhesive and cast iron dust; proprietary fillers can also be bought for the purpose. Before checking measurements on cast iron components, wipe with a rag as a layer of dust builds up which will give false readings.

BRASS
Like mild steel, brass comes in a variety of types; in fact, being an alloy of copper and zinc there are various grades, which give different degrees of hardness. Most used by the model engineer are quite soft. No lubricant is necessary unless prolonged work is being carried out. Swarf comes away as a fine spray on the softer metals and in small chips on the harder ones. Cutters that have been used on mild steel and not subsequently sharpened will cause heavy burring of the metal and a bad finish. The use of such cutters should therefore be avoided and it is wise to use separate cutters for each material.

BRONZE
This is an alloy of copper and tin, and some forms can be very tough. It is essential to use sharp tools that have not previously been used on steel or cast iron. A glazed finish indicates cutter wear and this will cause the material to harden. Heavy burrs also occur with worn cutters and these can be extremely difficult to remove. Swarf comes off either as fine chips or a spray depending on the coarseness of the cutter and the quality of the material. Cutting lubricants can help save cutter wear as heat tends to build up very quickly.

GUNMETAL
This is a form of bronze used in a cast form. It is often very soft material, and if cutters are not sharp the metal will compact or spread rather than cut. It hardens quickly with wear and it thus follows that worn cutters will cause it to harden. It also builds up heavy burrs which are difficult to remove. I have known worn cutters to cut considerably over size when used on gunmetal, so it is absolutely essential that cutters used on it are as sharp as possible.

ALUMINIUM
Like bronze, this material is obtainable in a whole range of qualities with various degrees of hardness. It is a very free cutting material but a great deal of heat is created when it is machined. It can easily be damaged when clamped to the table for machining because of its softness and it is as well to impose cardboard or similar materials between the clamps or vice jaws and the metal. Swarf formation varies considerably with the grade being machined, from a fine powder to long rolled chips, but the biggest problem is the build-up of waste material on the cutter and particularly between the teeth. A good supply of lubricant will help to avoid this but it may be necessary from time to time to stop operations and clear the build-up from the cutter, using a small piece of brass strip for the purpose.

MAGNESIUM ALLOY
It is unlikely that such material will be purchased, but as some

materials used by model engineers are, shall we say, 'donated' there is a possibility of getting hold of it unknowingly. It can be easily confused with some of the aluminium grades and it machines in much the same way, and the only reason I have included it in this list is because it is likely to be confused with aluminium alloys. The swarf from magnesium alloy is dangerous in that it can be ignited if care is not taken. Whilst the risk is small, it is as well to know of it.

PLASTICS

The various forms of plastic are not frequently used in model engineering but there may be times when there is need to machine them. The various grades are so diverse that it would take a whole chapter to describe all the properties. Most, however, will tend to swell and retract during machining, causing undersize slots or holes as the material contracts when the cutter has passed. The materials also have a habit of welding themselves back together after cutting. Slot drills are the best cutters to use as the coarser action caused by the two teeth lessens the heat build-up. Some plastics can give off toxic fumes when machined and under no circumstances should the operator smoke whilst carrying out machining operations, as there is a very distinct danger from these fumes if hot ash comes into contact with the swarf. Plastics can, surprisingly enough, cause considerable wear on cutters and when wear takes place the material tends to tear rather than cut.

CONCLUSION

I hope that this book has been both interesting and informative to readers, whether they are beginners to the subject or already have some knowledge of milling machines. There is no doubt that a milling machine used properly will enable a great deal of work to be carried out which would not otherwise be possible.

It has not been possible to go into the more unusual operations that may be carried out with the machine, many of which would require a volume of their own for the description. But, having gained a basic knowledge of the correct way of doing things, the more advanced operations are a matter of both imagination and experiment. Readers should start to think of using the machine at every possible opportunity and not just for the more obvious operations. It is surprising how an hour or so of pondering can reveal the answer to a problem which at first seems insoluble.

Coupling rods for a locomotive milled from solid material. The bearing holes can also be made on the milling machine using the table graduations to obtain extreme accuracy. The ends are rounded using a rotary table.

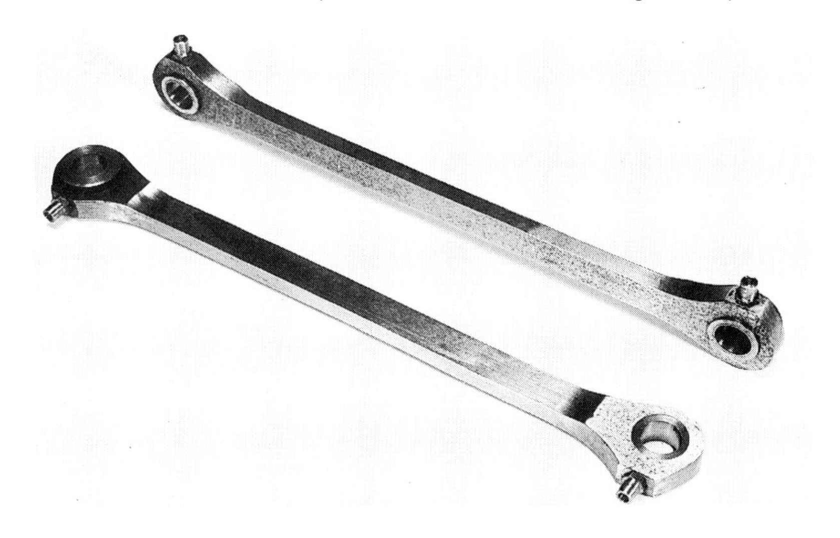

Eccentric straps and rods made with the aid of a milling machine. The eccentric strap has been milled flat and parted with a slitting saw. It is then bolted back together and the bore obtained with a boring head. Finally the slot for the rod is milled with a slot drill. The eccentric rod may be milled from solid using a large radius end mill or small fly cutter to obtain the radius. The slot again can be cut with a slot drill or slitting saw and the ends rounded using a rotary table.

Remember that the machine can be used to make its own attachment which in turn will allow more advanced operations to be carried out; in fact, the whole operation is self-generating. Many model engineers I know feel that making workshop equipment takes one away from making models, but my own view after many years' experience is that this is not absolutely true. If a special item is required then we must either go to an engineering firm and buy it or send away for it by mail order. As long as a suitable stock of metal is kept it is often quicker to make what we need, and it will of course be cheaper. There is a further bonus in making such items for ourselves. The more we use the machine, the more confident we will become in our ability. The more we learn how to make things, the quicker we will become. That in turn will make our efforts at model making more efficient.

This may all sound something like a lecture. I rather hope that instead it will be thought of as good sound advice. I hope then that I will have given readers both the encouragement and knowledge to help them improve their ability with a machine that increases tremendously the versatility of the workshop.

APPENDICES

APPENDIX 1 *FAULTS, CAUSES AND CURES*

A knowledge of faults that are likely to arise will be an aid to good milling. Here are outlined a few common problems to assist readers to trace the faults and remedy them.

FAULT	SYMPTOM	CAUSE	REMEDY
'Chatter'	Change of sound in machine. Excessive vibration. Shows as ridges and mottled finish.	Worn or loose cutter. Machine table not properly adjusted, work not properly tightened. Cutter speed too high. Feed rate too low.	Change or tighten cutter. Adjust machine. Tighten work. Change speed/feed rate.
Coarse finish	Ragged/discoloured swarf. Cutter making grating sound.	Worn cutter. Too coarse a feed. Too slow a cutter speed.	Change cutter. Alter speed/feed rate.
Wrong dimensions		Not allowing for backlash. Index ring loose on collar.	

APPENDIX 2 *ROTATIONAL SPEEDS OF MILLING CUTTERS*

One of the first things that an engineering apprentice would be taught was to work out the correct cutting speed for the work that was to be done. In the case of lathework this is found by taking the cutting speed of the metal as defined by the manufacturer, multiplying it by 12 in the case of imperial measurement and by a thousand if working in metric. The result is then dividened by the diameter of the bar times pi (3.1428) - i.e. its circumference. With a milling machine there is a variation which depends on the type of cutter in use. In industry this is fine. The buyer purchases so many thousand feet of metal with a known cutting speed and the operator can find the figure required by simple arithmetic as the quality of the cutter will also be know, here again data being obtained from the manufacturers who supply handbooks on their various products. The formula becomes so well used that it is one which will stay with the apprentice for the rest of his life and it will be second nature to use it.

Life for the model engineer is not like that. The metal we use is more often than not obtained from a model engineering supplier, or possibly is donated by a friend. Which quality it is we have absolutely no idea and probably neither does the supplier. Therefore, as we do not have access to the cutting speed of the metal and so cannot correctly work out the speed of cutter rotation, I have therefore prepared the following tables of suitable cutting speeds for the various metals most likely to be used, which will give the best results.

There is every chance that your machine will not have the correct speed amongst its limited range. If this is the case, take the nearest slower figure. Never use a faster speed as it may well lead to chatter, blunting and possibly even breaking of the cutter.

The speed at which the metal is fed into the cutter is also important and here again we have formulae for working out the correct rate of feed. This is fine where mechanical feeding is available, but as most home milling machines rely on hand feeding it is difficult to judge the correct rate of feed. The best advice is to take it easy. Do not feed too fast. Let the cutter feel its way through the work. Equally, though, too slow a feed can cause a rubbing effect. The machine will let you know if all is well as, with the correct feed, it will run comparitively quietly but will whine and scream if it is too slow, and chatter and shake if too fast.

Take care and use these tables and all should be well.

Cutter diameter Imperial (in)	Cutter diameter Metric (mm)	Cast iron and bronze	Mild steel	Brass and aluminium
		END MILLS		
3/32	2.5	2500	4000	7000
1/8	3.0	2000	3000	6000
3/16	4.0	1000	2000	5000
1/4	6.0	950	1604	3750
5/16	8.0	750	1200	3000
3/8	10.0	650	1000	2500
1/2	12.5	450	750	2000
5/8	16.0	350	600	1500
		SLOT DRILLS		
1/16	1.5	4000	6000	10000
3/32	2.5	2500	4000	8000
1/8	3.0	2000	3000	7000
3/16	4.0	1200	2000	6000
1/4	6.5	1000	1500	4000
5/16	8.0	800	1200	3000
3/8	10.0	700	1500	2750
1/2	12.5	500	750	2000
5/8	16.0	400	642	1750
		BALL-NOSED SLOT DRILLS		
1/16	1.5	4000	6000	10000
3/32	2.5	2750	4000	8000
1/8	3.0	2000	3000	7000
3/16	4.0	1250	2000	6000
1/4	6.0	1000	1500	4500
5/16	8.0	855	1000	3500
3/8	10.0	700	950	3000
1/2	12.5	500	800	2000
5/8	16.0	400	600	1500

Cutter diameter Imperial (in)	Cutter diameter Metric (mm)	Cast iron and bronze	Mild steel	Brass and aluminium
		FLY CUTTING		
1	25	120	150	225
1.5	35	80	100	150
2	50	60	80	120
2.5	62.5	50	60	100
3	75	40	50	80

APPENDIX 3 *TABLE OF CHORDS*

To find the chord of a division of a circle, take the figure shown against the number of required divisions and multiply it by the diameter of the circle.

No of divisions	Length of chord	No of divisions	Length of chord	No of divisions	Length of chord	No of divisions	Length of chord
		26	.1205	51	.0616	76	.0413
		27	.1161	52	.0604	77	.0408
3	.8660	28	.1120	53	.0592	78	.0403
4	.7071	29	.1081	54	.0581	79	.0398
5	.5878	30	.1045	55	.0571	80	.0393
6	.5000	31	.1012	56	.0561	81	.0388
7	.4339	32	.0980	57	.0551	82	.0383
8	.3827	33	.0951	58	.0541	83	.0378
9	.3420	34	.0923	59	.0532	84	.0374
10	.3090	35	.0896	60	.0523	85	.0370
11	.2817	36	.0872	61	.0515	86	.0365
12	.2583	37	.0848	62	.0507	87	.0361
13	.2393	38	.0826	63	.0499	88	.0537
14	.2225	39	.0805	64	.0491	89	.0353
15	.2079	40	.0785	65	.0483	90	.0349
16	.1951	41	.0765	66	.0476	91	.0345
17	.1838	42	.0747	67	.0469	92	.0341
18	.1736	43	.0730	68	.0462	93	.0338
19	.1646	44	.0713	69	.0455	94	.0334
20	.1564	45	.0698	70	.0499	95	.0331
21	.1490	46	.0682	71	.0442	96	.0327
22	.1423	47	.0668	72	.0436	97	.0324
23	.1362	48	.0654	73	.0430	98	.0321
24	.1305	49	.0641	74	.0424	99	.0317
25	.1253	50	.0628	75	.0419	100	.0314

INDEX